Instructor's Manual

to accompany

SO-AGK-481

Teaching Science in Elementary and Middle School Classrooms
A Project-Based Approach

Second Edition

Joseph S. Krajcik
University of Michigan

Charlene M. Czerniak
University of Toledo

Carl F. Berger
University of Michigan

Prepared by
Rebecca Schneider
University of Toledo

Boston   Burr Ridge, IL   Dubuque, IA   Madison, WI   New York   San Francisco   St. Louis
Bangkok   Bogotá   Caracas   Kuala Lumpur   Lisbon   London   Madrid   Mexico City
Milan   Montreal   New Delhi   Santiago   Seoul   Singapore   Sydney   Taipei   Toronto

Instructor's Manual to accompany
TEACHING SCIENCE IN ELEMENTARY AND MIDDLE SCHOOL CLASSROOMS
Joseph S. Krajcik, Charlene M. Czerniak, Carl F. Berger

Published by McGraw-Hill, an imprint of The McGraw-Hill Companies, Inc., 1221 Avenue of the Americas, New York, NY 10020. Copyright © 2003 (1999) by The McGraw-Hill Companies, Inc.

1 2 3 4 5 6 7 8 9 0 QSR/QSR 0 9 8 7 6 5 4 3 2

ISBN 0-07-248675-9

www.mhhe.com

TABLE OF CONTENTS

PREFACE

This instructor's manual is designed to support you in educating elementary and middle grade science teachers. To begin this task I present lesson and assessment ideas that are consistent with the approach to teaching science presented in *Teaching Science in Elementary and Middle School Classrooms: A Project-Based Approach*. Learning environments that include inquiry, collaboration, and embedded technology use are beneficial for teachers and students alike. Moreover, these experiences can model appropriate instructional practices for those learning about teaching. Reflection and revision are also important features of any learning environment. I highlight multiple opportunities for your students to reflect on their own learning, think about how and what students learn, and revisit their ideas and plans. Finally, both novice and experienced teachers benefit from experiences that support reflection on classroom practice. Opportunities for your students to learn from classrooms as an observer or teacher and to apply what they have learned about teaching children science are emphasized throughout. The work of preparing of elementary and middle grades teachers to teach science for all children has never been more important. I hope you find the ideas presented in this manual helpful.

Your Students

Although the text is intended primarily for university students studying to become elementary and middle grade science teachers, the material is also suitable for the practicing teacher striving to find new, exciting approaches to science teaching. Learning how to teach science to elementary and middle grade students is complex. The ideas addressing important questions and the number of strategies presented in the text will challenge both novice and experienced teachers.

This instructor's manual also presents numerous ideas and strategies to support you in educating elementary and middle grade science teachers. The overall sequence and type of lesson and assessment ideas included in this manual are appropriate for all audiences. However, it will be important for you to adapt the lesson and assessment ideas to meet the specific learning needs of your students. Novice teachers may need more time to explore specific strategies or examples. Experienced teachers may need help meshing new ideas with existing lessons or curriculum frameworks. You will also want to consider the local communities where your students will teach. Teachers preparing to teach in urban, rural, or suburban settings will each have unique challenges to address in their classrooms. One obvious modification you will need to make is how to connect to classrooms. Pre-service teachers can observe and interact with children as part of field experiences in classrooms. Practicing teachers can reflect on their own teaching and enact new lessons in their classrooms.

Organization and Coverage

Each chapter of this instructor's manual is aligned with the material presented in the text and includes the following components.

1. Chapter Overview
2. Chapter Learning Performances
3. Lesson Ideas
4. Discussion Questions
5. Assessment Ideas
6. Resources

The overview for each chapter describes how the chapter builds on previous chapters and contributes to future chapters. The main ideas from the text are highlighted. Together with the listed learning performances and assessment ideas, you should have a good idea of what students will learn in the chapter. Lesson and assessment ideas are described in more detail below.

Throughout this manual you will find tips to help you in planning and supporting your students' learning. These ideas point out areas where your students may have difficulty or strategies that may be useful. Tips are highlighted by shaded boxes.

> **Tip:** Although each idea is presented in connection with a specific lesson or assessment idea, you will find that many of the ideas can be applied to activities described in other chapters.

<u>Visual Resources:</u> You will also find references to figures or other material from the text that would be useful as transparencies or class handouts. These materials are available in the Instructor's area of the Online Learning Center as black-line masters for you to print and copy.

Resources to support you and your students are listed for each chapter. Text resources will give you more information about a topic or additional ideas and suggestions. You may decide to include some of the text materials as part of your class' reading list, particularly if your class is an advanced or graduate-level methods course. Internet resources will direct you to on-line materials such as curriculum materials, educational software, or examples of students' work. You can access all of these sites directly in the Instructor's area of the Online Learning Center. Web addresses will be updated there as changes are made.

Lesson ideas

The lesson ideas in each chapter are organized by same chapter sections as the text. This organization should make it easy for you to find what you need and to align this information with what your students are reading. Also, each portfolio activity is listed within each section in the order in which they appear in the text. In general, lessons begin by exploring your students' initial ideas based on their own experiences, offer new experiences with project-based science, compare various instructional methods in light of new ideas and experiences, and finally support your students in developing their own project-based instructional plans. Revisiting ideas and revising plans are emphasized throughout.

Project Example

Your students need to understand and experience specific strategies and features of project-based science. For example, in Chapter 4, *How Are Scientific Investigations Developed?*, your students will need opportunities to do investigations and reflect on the components and strategies used by you to guide them in their investigations. This will help your students understand what an investigation is, what it is not, and how investigations support students in learning science.

> **Tip:** Methods courses can model project-based science by connecting lessons across chapters to answer a driving question. One example question is, *How do I plan for project-based science in my classroom?*

A project example is described through out this manual. This project leads students to explore equilibrium, evidence-based conclusions, and boat design as they answer *How can I predict if my boat will float?* You can decide to use this example or develop one of your own. In either case, following an example project throughout the various chapter topics not only models project-based science but also gives you and your students an example of each aspect of project-based science for reflection and discussion. It will also serve as a model for your students when they begin to develop their own units.

Project Development

Next, your students need to take these new ideas and put them into practice. This means your students should develop specific lesson or unit plans. For example, your students can develop plans for an investigation lesson they could use with their own students. These plans should incorporate the components and strategies that made their own investigations valuable learning experiences.

> **Tip:** Developing and sharing plans is an excellent opportunity to discuss the benefits and challenges of specific strategies and project-based science features. For example, how do teachers make sure they give students enough support yet let students participate in decisions and questions?

Whenever possible you should incorporate classroom experiences. Your students will benefit from multiple opportunities to interact with children. This can include observing children as they interact with their teacher and each other and participate in specific lessons and activities; conversations with children about their science ideas; and guiding children in lessons and activities based on project-based ideas such as investigations. For pre-service teachers this can be accomplished in field experiences or student teaching. In-service teachers have the benefit of being able to work in their own classrooms.

Assessment ideas

Assessment ideas for the chapter are described following the lesson ideas. You might, however, find it helpful to read over the assessment ideas first, along with the chapter learning performances. This will give you a clear idea of the goals for each lesson idea and will help you focus your lessons on aspects of student understanding you will assess. In general, assessment ideas are closely related to the lesson ideas. Artifacts students create to support their learning also can demonstrate their understanding.

As described in Chapters 8 and 9, assessments should include measuring students' understandings in situations that match real life, helping teachers plan instruction, continuously monitoring student progress, measuring academic progress fairly and accurately, helping students to become self-regulated learners, and assessing progress of individual students. Assessments should provide authentic and meaningful feedback to the instructor. Assessment in an inquiry-based college classroom should involve students in

- actively generating a response,

- accomplishing complex tasks, and

- solving realistic and authentic problems.

Each of the main assessment types described below is included because it matches this description. These assessments not only will help you and your students to evaluate their progress and understanding, but will also model appropriate assessment strategies for your students.

Portfolio Assessment

One assessment idea is to require specific portfolio activities to be included in your students' portfolios. This can be a formative assessment giving you information about your students' developing understanding as they participate in class activities and discussions. Reading portfolio responses also allows you to read what each student is thinking, not just those who speak up in class. Self assessment of portfolio entries can help your students gauge their progress and determine where to concentrate their efforts.

Project Example

Another assessment strategy is to include an assessment component in the example project. For example, students' investigation designs can illustrate their understating of how to select and control variables. Likewise, their ideas about good investigation questions can be demonstrated by asking students to develop and justify their own investigation questions. In addition, asking students to describe the science ideas that explain why or how their final project artifact works and then scoring their responses with an appropriate rubric will engage them in this task and will model project-based assessment.

Chapter Specific Assessments

Chapter-specific assessment ideas match the specific topics in each chapter. These include application and evaluation using specified criteria, reflection on examples or experiences, and artifacts such as concept maps.

> **Tip:** Assessments can become valuable learning opportunities when comments from instructors and peers describe what was well done and give suggestions for improvement.

Project Development

Finally, individual components and whole projects developed by your students are valuable evidence of their ability to bring these ideas into the classroom. Although you will certainly want to include feedback as part of all your assessments, this is particularly important for project development. Developing projects can be difficult and complex. Your students will need to revise portions of their plans. Your feedback will be an invaluable resource to support students in revising and improving their ideas.

Resources

Text Resources

Borko, H., and Putnam, R. T. (1996). Learning to teach. In R. C. Calfee and D. C. Berliner (Eds.), *Handbook of Educational Psychology*. New York: Macmillan.

Loucks-Horsley, S., Hewson, P. W., Love, N., and Stiles, K. E. (1998). *Designing Professional Development for Teachers of Science and Mathematics*. Thousand Oaks, CA: Corwin Press.

Putnam, R. T., and Borko, H. (2000). What do new views of knowledge and thinking have to say about research on teacher learning? *Educational Researcher*, 29(1): 4–15.

Wiggins, G., and McTighe, J. (1998). *Understanding by Design*. Alexandria, VA: ASCD Association for Supervision and Curriculum Development.

Internet Resources

You can access this site directly in the Instructor's area of the Online Learning Center. Web addresses will be updated there as changes are made.

MERLOT (http://www.merlot.org/Home.po): MERLOT is a free and open resource designed primarily for faculty and students of higher education. Links to on-line learning materials are collected here, along with annotations such as peer reviews and assignments.

Acknowledgement

I would like to thank Joe Krajcik, Charlene Czerniak, and Carl Berger for giving me the opportunity to write this instructor's manual. I also appreciate their support and guidance as they helped me to better understand how students and teachers learn. They have been extraordinary mentors. I would also like to acknowledge Barbara Crawford who wrote the instructor's manual to accompany the first edition of the text. Her work made writing this manual easier.

CHAPTER 1
WHY AND HOW SHOULD I TEACH SCIENCE TO CHILDREN?

Chapter Overview

This first chapter introduces students to project-based science and the importance of teaching science to all elementary and middle school students. Unlike other approaches, project-based science situates the learning of science in questions that children find meaningful and relevant to their lives. Using technology, students investigate, develop artifacts, collaborate, and make products to show what they have learned. This exciting approach to teaching science to children has a solid foundation in educational theory and addresses the national goals for and standards of science education. Yet, it is unlike how science is taught in most classrooms today. This approach will be new to most of your students.

This introductory chapter also gives students an overview of each chapter and the features of the book. Each chapter begins with several scenarios designed to help your students envision various classroom scenes that will be discussed in the chapter. Portfolio activities throughout the text encourage students to think about ideas before they continue reading. These activities engage students in tasks that will help them connect their reading to student learning and classroom practice. Both the scenarios and the portfolio activities can be topics for class discussion.

Chapter Learning Performances

- Describe the primary features of project-based science.

- Compare and contrast project-based science with reading about science, direct instruction, and process science.

- Explain how project-based science reflects the nature of science.

- Justify why young learners should learn science.

- Summarize the primary features of our national science goals.

- Explain the value of using project-based science to meet national goals and standards, particularly the goals of encouraging females and minorities in science.

Lesson Ideas

The lesson ideas described here and throughout this manual are designed to be consistent with project-based science. You will find it helpful for your own planning to preview each of the chapters for ideas that you should incorporate early in your course. For example, here in Chapter 1 your students are beginning to work together and share ideas. Chapter 6 describes many strategies to help students collaborate in small groups, as a whole class, and with others outside of the classroom. Setting up a class email list is one idea in particular that you should begin at the start of your course. Other chapters that are particularly helpful for advance planning are Chapter 5 on technology and Chapter 9 on assessment.

An Overview of Project-Based Science

This chapter serves as an introduction to the entire text and your course. A good way to begin is to give your students an overview of the course and project-based science. This includes an orientation to resources in the text and a brief discussion of the main learning performances and activities. Each topic will have more meaning when your students can connect ideas to the larger picture. Your students also can begin to gather ideas for questions or topics they would like to explore or develop during the course.

> **Tip:** Explain to your students that the portfolio activities are located in places throughout the text to help them understand the ideas before proceeding with the next section of reading. Your students should do each of the portfolio activities you assign as they come to them in the reading rather than completing them all at once at the end of the chapter.

This is a good time to introduce students to a driving question for the course. Examples of appropriate driving questions include *How can I help all students learn science?*, *How should science be taught to young learners?*, and *How do I plan for project-based science?* The class driving question can guide students throughout the course as they learn specific ideas and strategies and develop their own plans for teaching science to children.

Initial Experiences, Ideas, and Goals for Teaching Science

After an introduction to the course, one of the first things you should do is have your students express their initial ideas and previous experiences with science teaching and learning. It is important for your students to make these ideas explicit. Like students, teachers learn by building on what they already know. You will be able to modify your plan based on your students' ideas. Your students will be able to see their progress.

Portfolio Activity 1.1 *What Are Your Elementary and Middle School Science Experiences?:* This first portfolio activity will help your students begin to think about their experiences with science teaching. If your students are experienced teachers, you can have them also reflect on how they teach science. Preservice teachers will draw mainly on their experiences as a student in grades K-12 or more recently in college. It will be important to revisit your students' descriptions of their experiences at the end of the course.

Discuss Portfolio Activity 1.1 or a similar activity during class. Give your students time to reflect and write their descriptions individually. Have several students share their stories with the class in a whole-class discussion.

Portfolio Activity 1.2 *What Are the Characteristics and Challenges of Each of the Scenarios?:* Discussion of this activity can be included in the class discussion of Portfolio Activity 1.1. Students' stories can be compared to each of the scenarios. Ask your students what type of teaching best describes their experiences.

What Is Science?

Science Concept Map

Your students' ideas about science will also influence their learning about teaching. One way to have your students express their ideas about science is to have them create a concept map. They can begin by brainstorming a list of words related to science as a whole class. Then, using this list, students can spend 15 to 20 minutes sketching out their own concept maps of science. Student can choose to add or delete words from the class brainstorm list. The next step is to share their maps with a partner to create one common map they both can agree on. Groups can then share their maps with the class. Each student should write a short statement describing their group's map and in what ways he or she agrees or disagrees with the group's map and why.

> **Tip:** If your students are not familiar with concept mapping, you will need to guide them through the process with an example. Chapter 7, "How Do I Develop and Use Benchmark Lessons?," describes how to create concept maps and gives an example.

An alternative method to help students describe their ideas about science is to have students make a sketch of what a scientist looks like. Ask students to share their sketches with another person. Conduct a class discussion compiling results and develop a class description of a scientist. You could bring up the issue of stereotypes and the sources of these stereotypes in society. What implications do these have for teaching elementary science?

Portfolio Activity 1.3 *Where's the Other Film Canister?* This is a good activity to do in class. It can be very difficult to determine the contents of the canister by sound or weight, particularly if your students use more than one object in the film canister.

> **Tip:** Your students may expect Portfolio Activity 1.3 to be simple and will want to put multiple objects in their film canisters. They may also be quite sure their conclusions are correct until they open the canisters!

Why Should Young Learners Study Science?

Portfolio Activity 1.4 *Why Should Children Learn Science?:* An extension to Portfolio Activity 1.4 is to have a class discussion of scientific literacy. Have students read the first chapter in *Science for All Americans*. Conduct a discussion of what it means to be scientifically literate. What can elementary and middle school teachers do to help students toward this goal by grade 12?

Goals of Science Education

Portfolio Activity 1.5 *What Are Your Personal Goals for Science Education?:* This is an interesting activity to discuss before exploring the national goals for science education.

Have your students spend some time becoming familiar with each of the documents describing national goals. These include *National Science Education Standards* (NRC, 1996), *Science for All Americans* and *Benchmarks for Science Literacy* from Project 2061 (AAAS, 1993; 1990), and the *National Science Teachers Association Position Statement: Elementary School Science* (NSTA, 2002). More recently, Project 2061 has mapped many of the benchmarks across grade levels in *Atlas for Science Literacy* (AAAS, 2001). These will be important sources of content descriptions and ideas when your students begin developing their plans for specific lesson or units in the following chapters.

After students have read about and looked at the national goals, they can revisit Portfolio Activity 1.5. Discuss how the national goals compare to their goals.

How Do the Current National Goals Compare with Project-Based Science?

Portfolio Activity 1.6 *Case Study of an Elementary or Middle Grade Classroom:* This activity is a nice way for students to become familiar with their field placement school. In-service teachers also will find it valuable to evaluate their school's science program in comparison to national goals.

Portfolio Activity 1.7 *Questions about Science Teaching:* Reading what your students write for this activity is an excellent method for you to find out what your students are expecting from your course. This will help you in your own planning.

In the last activity students write down their questions about teaching science to elementary and middle school students and questions they have about project-based science. At the end of the course, students will revisit these questions and self-assess what they have learned.

Discussion Questions

Many people have not experienced the kind of science teaching that involves students asking questions and carrying out investigations with others. Why is it important to change our approach to teaching science today?

How is project-based science different from the process science approach to teaching science?

Why is it important for children in the early grades to learn science when it might be more important to learn reading and math skills? Select one topic or concept in science that you think would be essential for children to learn. Defend your selection.

How can a teacher meet the demands of covering a range of science topics if this teacher spends several weeks involving students in investigating one driving question?

If scientific theories can change, why is it important for people to learn these theories?

Think of a current issue in the news that relates to science. What scientific concepts would it be important for elementary and middle school children to understand about this issue?

In what ways could an elementary or middle school teacher help children develop a positive attitude toward science?

Assessment Ideas

At this stage, assessment should focus on identifying students' initial ideas and experiences. This will guide you in planning future lessons. It will also help both you and your students see how their ideas change and develop during this course.

Portfolio Assessment

Although students have just begun their portfolios, you will want to read their responses. Students are describing their experiences, ideas, and goals. These descriptions are invaluable to help you in planning your course. You also will want to revisit these descriptions so both you and your students will be able to see their progress. Portfolio Activities 1.1, *What Are Your Elementary and Middle School Science Experiences?*, 1.2, *What Are the Characteristics and Challenges of Each of the Scenarios?*, and 1.5, *What Are Your Personal Goals for Science Education?* illustrate your students' experiences, ideas, and goals explicitly.

Science Concept Map

Again, the goal here should be to understand your students' initial ideas about science and thus teaching science. You can evaluate maps for completeness and complexity. Are there areas of science missing from the map, such as the processes of science or the nature of scientific evidence? Is the map linear, or is it weblike, showing an integrated understanding? Are the links appropriate? Is there an appropriate hierarchy? Also, read the students' short descriptions of what they liked or would change about their maps. These descriptions also will give you information about their ideas.

Resources

Text Resources

American Association for the Advancement of Science. (1990). *Science for All Americans*. New York: Oxford University Press.

American Association for the Advancement of Science. (1993). *Benchmarks for Science Literacy*. New York: Oxford University Press.

American Association for the Advancement of Science. (2001). *Atlas of Science Literacy*. Washington, D.C.: American Association for the Advancement of Science and National Science Teachers Association Press.

Crawford, B. A. (1998). The scientific method: A fatal flaw. *Science Scope*, April 1998, 50–52.

Crawford, B. A. (1998). The poisons project: Creating an inquiry-based unit. *Science Scope*, February 1998, 18–22.

Driver, R., Leach, J., Miller, R., and Scott, P. (1996). *Young People's Images of Science*. Philadelphia: Open University Press.

National Research Council. (1996). *National Science Education Standards*. Washington, D.C.: National Academy Press.

National Science Teachers Association. (2002). *Teaching Teachers: Bringing First-Rate Science to the Elementary Classroom*. Washington, D.C.: National Science Teachers Association.

Internet Resources

You can access all of these sites directly in the Instructor's area of the Online Learning Center. Web addresses will be updated there as changes are made.

Benchmarks for Science Literacy (http://www.project2061.org/tools/benchol/bolframe.htm): Entire on-line text of the Benchmarks for Science Literacy from Project 2061 of the American Association for the Advancement of Science.

National Academy of Sciences (http://www.nas.edu): Includes links to entire on-line text of the *National Science Education Standards*. Browse contents and abstracts of *Proceedings of the National Academy of Sciences* with opportunity to access thousands of scientific reports; links to description of books and resources for educators and scientists working together.

National Science Education Standards (http://www.nap.edu/books/0309053269/html): Entire on-line text of the National Science Education Standards from the National Research Council.

National Science Teachers Association (http://www.nsta.org): Professional organization for teachers of science at all grade levels elementary to college; resource includes on-line journals—*Science and Children* for elementary science teachers and *Science Scope* for middle grades science teachers—and recommendations for teaching science and position statements of NSTA.

Project 2061 (http://www.project2061.org): Describes *Project 2061* background and goals and the guiding document, *Science for All Americans*; links to on-line text of *Benchmarks for Science Literacy*; links to on-line text of *Blueprints*, description of *Resources for Science Literacy*; and highlights the important role of teachers in current science reform.

The Third International Mathematics and Science Study TIMMS (http://nces.ed.gov/TIMSS): Data on the mathematics and science achievement of our students compared to that of students in other countries.

CHAPTER 2
HOW DO CHILDREN CONSTRUCT UNDERSTANDING IN SCIENCE?

Chapter Overview

Before exploring the features of project-based in detail in Chapters 3 to 9, it is important to understand how students learn science. This chapter describes current theories of how children learn, and how the teaching approach of project-based science is connected to social constructivist learning theory. Students need to construct content, procedural, and metacognitive knowledge to develop understanding. The ultimate goal of project-based science is the development of students' integrated understandings.

In a social constructivist model of teaching, students are actively engaged with phenomena, use and apply knowledge, use multiple representations of understandings, use learning communities, and focus on authentic tasks, all aspects of project-based science. This model addresses the problem of children's lack of in-depth understandings of science when taught with teaching methods of the past. In a project-based science approach, investigations allow learners to engage in the features of the social constructivist model of teaching.

Teachers can play an important role in scaffolding student learning. Scaffolding allows learners to take part in cognitive activities just beyond the reach of their cognitive development. Teachers can scaffold learners by modeling, coaching, sequencing, reducing complexity, marking critical features, and using visual tools.

Tasks in school need to be authentic for children to find them meaningful. The aspects of authentic tasks are driving questions, the relevance of questions or topics to students, the connection of learning to students' lives outside of school, and the emergence of science concepts and principles when they are needed. Technology tools play an important role in supporting teachers and students in project-based science.

Chapter Learning Performances

- Explain the difference between inert and meaningful knowledge.

- Describe the three types of knowledge—content, procedural, and metacognitive.

- Critique examples of teaching to determine if they represent receptional or transformation approaches to teaching and learning.

- Explain what is meant by social constructivism and describe the various features of a social constructivist model of teaching.

- Develop a lesson based on the social constructivist model of teaching.

- Apply the idea of scaffolding to help children accomplish a difficult learning task.

- Discuss how authentic tasks help women and minorities participate and stay interested in science.

Lesson Ideas

Student Understanding

A good way to introduce the topic of student understanding is to have your students think about their own understanding. Have students explain their ideas about a phenomenon such as the one described in Portfolio Activity 2.1. Then have your students view a video or read about students' ideas on the subject.

Portfolio Activity 2.1 *Thinking about Your Own Understanding:* After students have discussed their own ideas, show clips from the video *Biology: Lesson Pulled from Thin Air* Program 2, from the Private Universe Workshop Series. Select segments from the first part of the video in which an eighth grader and a seventh grader are interviewed about their ideas on the structure of matter. You can return to this topic and show more segments from the video later when your students are discussing models of teaching.

Portfolio Activity 2.1 describes one example from life science that your students can do in class. You can also do some of the other examples described in the text or from other sources. The first Private Universe videotape depicts interviews of Harvard graduates on graduation day. In this tape graduates are asked to respond to the question, "What causes the seasons?" Before showing the videotape, ask students to write down a brief answer to this question: "Why do we have seasons?" Suggest that students make a drawing to explain this. Next, give students time in class to share their ideas with a partner. Then show the videotape. This is a classic study that illustrates the lack of in-depth understanding of an important science concept by top-notch university graduates.

> **Tip:** It likely that your students will have some of the same ideas as the students in the examples.

Investigating Students' Science Ideas

Talking to children is an excellent way to learn about students' science ideas. First, have your students practice their interviewing skills in class. Working in groups of three, each student should have a turn to interview another student. The third student in each group observes the interview and give feedback to the interviewer on questions that could have been asked or questions that should have been worded differently. You should supply the interview topics. Because students are in groups of three, three topics will give each student a fresh topic for each interview. *Probing Understanding* by White and Gunstone is a good source of ideas for interview strategies, topics, and example interviews.

> **Tip:** Students report learning as much from observing the interview as they do from practicing being the interviewer. Make sure each student has the opportunity to observe an interview.

Portfolio Activity 2.2 *Investigate Young Learners' Ideas Regarding Physical and Chemical Change:* If possible, have your students tape-record the interview and later record notes from the tape. If taping is not possible, students will need to take notes during the interviews.

Have your students bring their interview notes to class to share and discuss. Begin by having your students share their interview stories in small groups. Next, have each group share their ideas with the whole class. Have your students focus on the following discussion questions.

- Do you think the child understood the science concept? Why?

- Did the child say anything that surprised you or that you found interesting?

- What are possible experiences that might explain the child's ideas? Why?

- What did you learn from the interview?

Another approach is to have students read an excerpt from *Children's Ideas in Science* by Driver or *Conceptual Change in Childhood* by Carey. Have your students select an interview topic from their reading. Using the same directions as in Portfolio Activity 2.2, your students can interview one or two students on this topic. When students share their interview notes in class, ask them to compare their students' ideas with those described in the reading.

> **Tip:** Children's ideas about science are not always obvious. It is easy for teachers to believe students understand science ideas when they use science words and repeat correct explanations. However, shallow understanding is revealed when students are asked to explain their ideas in more detail. Your students may be surprised by some of their students' ideas.

Visual Resources: Figure 2.3 Understanding as a Function of Knowledge Accumulation and Knowledge Integration, available in the Instructor's area of the Online Learning Center.

Models of Teaching

Return to the discussion begun in Portfolio Activity 2.1 *Thinking about Your Own Understanding*. Now have students think about how students might have constructed these ideas. If your students have similar ideas, they can describe why these ideas make sense to them. Continue with clips from the Private Universe video *Biology: Lesson Pulled from Thin Air*. Select segments from the classroom lessons on photosynthesis and the following interview with students. Discuss why these hands-on lessons did not result in the understanding hoped for by the teacher. Then select segments describing the lesson designed to build from students' initial ideas and the following interview with students. Discuss what was different about this lesson and why students' ideas changed.

> **Tip:** Many teachers misunderstand transformational models to mean that teachers should not tell students the answers and should not offer help. This idea makes sense when we tell teachers that receptional models, which assume students should be given or told the correct ideas, are not the best models for helping students learn science. You will want to emphasize that transformational models assume students need guidance and support.

Social Construction of Knowledge

Learning Theory Concept Map

Concept mapping can help your students work through and organize their ideas about student understanding and learning. The class as a group can select concepts that should be included in everyone's concept map. Then, using this list, students can spend 15 to 20 minutes sketching out their own concept maps of how students learn. Student can choose to add concepts to the class list. The next step is to share their maps with a partner to create one common map they both can agree on. Groups can then share their maps with the class. Each student should write a short statement describing their group's map and in what ways he or she agrees or disagrees with the group's map and why. Students can revisit these concept maps periodically to add ideas from future chapters.

Portfolio Activity 2.3 *Recognizing and Evaluating a Social Constructivist Lesson:* Do this activity in class. In small groups, students discuss and evaluate each classroom description. Then groups report and explain their evaluation in a whole-class discussion. This discussion includes suggestions for revising the lessons based on the evaluation.

> **Tip:** Your students will find that neither lesson has all the features of a social constructivist classroom. They will also find that coming to a decision on each category is not easy.

A Social Constructivist Model of Teaching

Visual Resources: Figure 2.4 Dale's Cone of Experience, available in the Instructor's area of the Online Learning Center.

Portfolio Activity 2.4 *Determining Levels of Concreteness and Abstractness*

Visual Resources: Figure 2.5 Compare and Contrast Diagram to Represent a Concept, available in the Instructor's area of the Online Learning Center.

Topic Development

At this early stage your students are just beginning to think about a topic for the unit they will develop in this course. As they select a topic, have your students read descriptions of concepts in *Standards* or *Benchmarks*. This will give them an idea of what is an appropriate level of student understanding for each concept. Next, students can interview a student or research students' ideas in sources such as *Children's Ideas in Science* by Driver. This will give them an idea where students may have difficulty in understanding concepts. This information will help them plan lessons that will match students' learning needs in future chapters.

> **Tip:** Novice teachers are naturally concerned with their own learning. You will have to encourage them to think about student learning.

Portfolio Activity 2.5 *Developing a Social Constructivist Lesson*

Visual Resources: Figure 2.6 Visual Tool to Represent Steps in a Task, available in the Instructor's area of the Online Learning Center.

Discussion Questions

Give examples of teaching a science concept or skill using each of these three approaches: (1) receptional; (2) transformational; and (3) contextualized. Discuss how you would use different approaches to teach different concepts and skills. For example, what approach would you use to best teach your students (a) how to use a microscope? (b) how a light bulb lights? (c) that science is tentative? (d) how a musical instrument produces sounds of different pitch?

What are some ways in which you could determine your students' prior understandings of a science topic such as light and shadows? What kind of questions could you ask your students? What are some strategies you could use to determine what all your students understood before teaching a unit on light and shadows?

Social constructivism suggests that learning occurs in context. For example, the topic of decomposing could relate to a family building and maintaining a compost pile. Suggest a context that might be appropriate for elementary and middle school students for the following science topics: density, light, matter, magnetism, plants, growth and development, animal behavior, rocks and minerals, and water.

Find a plan for a science lesson and identify the parts of the social constructivist model of teaching (active engagement with phenomena; using and applying knowledge; multiple representations; use of learning communities; and the role of authentic tasks). Are any parts of this model missing? If so, how could you adapt this lesson to include these missing parts?

Children often contribute ideas during class discussions that are not consistent with scientists' ideas. How would you handle this in an elementary classroom?

Assessment Ideas

Portfolio Assessment

One assessment strategy is to have your students record their work continuously but collect their portfolios only periodically. Activity 2.2, *Investigate Young Learners' Ideas Regarding Physical and Chemical Change*, can be included as part of the assessment Investigating Students' Science Ideas described below. Activity 2.3, *Recognizing and Evaluating a Social Constructivist Lesson*, will illustrate your students' ability to recognize the features of a social constructivist lesson. Students also can evaluate their own lesson ideas with this same evaluation scheme.

Investigating Students' Science Ideas

Have your student write a summary of their interview with a student. They should include a brief description of the topic, interview questions, and the student's responses. They should then write their individual responses to the discussion questions.

- Do you think the child understood the science concept? Why?

- Did the child say anything that surprised you or that you found interesting?

- What are possible experiences that might explain the child's ideas? Why?

- What did you learn from the interview?

Learning Theory Concept Map

Your students' concept maps can be evaluated for their understanding of social constructivism. You should not expect complete understanding at this early stage. Your students will learn much more about this learning model as they explore applications of this theory in the remaining chapters. You can evaluate maps for completeness and complexity. Are there aspects of the learning model obviously missing from the map? Is the map linear, or is it weblike, showing an integrated understanding? Are the links appropriate? Is there an appropriate hierarchy? Also, read their short descriptions of what they liked or would change about their maps. These descriptions also will give you information about their ideas.

Topic Development

Your students are only just beginning to think about developing their own lessons. You will want to give them feedback on their early ideas. Make sure they have chosen important topics that are included in *Standards, Benchmarks*, or local standards. Your student should also be thinking about students' ideas on the topic.

Resources

Text Resources

Presidents and Fellows of Harvard University (1995). *The Private Universe Project*. South Burlington, VT: Annenberg/CPB Math and Science Collection. (Video is available from the Annenberg/CPB Math and Science Collection, P.O. Box 2345, S. Burlington, VT 05407.)

American Association for the Advancement of Science (1990). *Science for All Americans*. New York: Oxford University Press.

American Association for the Advancement of Science (1993). *Benchmarks for Science Literacy*. New York: Oxford University Press.

Carey, S. (1992). *Conceptual Change in Childhood*. Cambridge, MA: MIT Press.

Driver, R., Guesne, E., and Tiberghien, A. (1985). *Children's Ideas in Science*. United Kingdom: Open University Press.

Driver, R. (1989). The construction of scientific knowledge in school classrooms. In R. Millar, (Ed.), *Doing Science: Images of Science in Science Education*. London: The Falmer Press.

Driver, R., Asoko, H., Leach, J., Mortimer, E., and Scott, P. (1994). Constructing scientific knowledge in the classroom. *Educational Researcher*, 23: 4.

Duckworth, E. (1996). *"The Having of Wonderful Ideas" and Other Essays on Teaching and Learning*. 2nd ed. New York: Teachers College Press.

McGilly, K. (1996). *Classroom Lessons: Integrating Cognitive Theory and Classroom Practice*. Cambridge, MA: Bradford.

National Research Council (1996). *National Science Education Standards*. Washington, D.C.: National Academy Press.

National Research Council (2000). *Inquiry and the National Science Education Standards*. Washington, D.C.: National Academy Press.

Tinker, R. (1996). *Thinking about Science*. http://www.concord.org: Concord Consortium.

Vygotsky, L.S. (1978). *Mind in Society: The Development of Higher Psychological Processes* (M. Cole, V. John-Steiner, S. Scriber, and E Souberman, Eds. and transiators). Cambridge, MA: Harvard University Press.

White, R., and Gunstone, R. (1992). *Probing Understanding*. London: Farmer Press.

Internet Resources

You can access all of these sites directly on the Instructor's area of the Online Learning Center. Web addresses will be updated there as changes are made.

Annenburg/CPB Channel (http://www.learner.org): On-line broadcast of Annenburg programs including Private Universe Project in Science workshop series.

Dale's Cone of Experience (http://www.nwrel.org/cnorse/booklets/achieve/table6.html): On-line diagram of Dale's Cone of Experience.

Earthscape (http://www.und.edu/instruct/eng/fkarner/earth.htm): A learner's guide to the environment. Earthscape invites you outdoors to investigate Earth systems, landscapes, and environmental challenges. In the Learning Lab, you can go to our Ask a Scientist section to get answers to your questions, learn about experiments, and other cool activities, games, and exercises.

Funderstanding (http://www.funderstanding.com/about_learning.cfm): Provides overviews of different learning theories; links to book reviews

Graphic Organizers (http://www.graphic.org): News about a variety of graphical organizers including Kidspiration software for concept mapping.

Jean Piaget Archives (http://www.unige.ch/piaget): Biography and writings of Jean Piaget housed at the University of Geneva

Pathwise **Graphic** **Organizers** (http://www.ncrel.org/sdrs/areas/issues/students/learning/lr1grorg.htm): Examples of several graphic organizers with descriptions of how they can be used by students.

Science Technology and Society Critical and Cultural Studies in Science (http://www.dcu.ie/~comms/sts/books.html): Includes extensive reading list of books related to science, society, and technology housed at the Dublin City University.

The Third International Mathematics and Science Study TIMMS (http://nces.ed.gov/TIMSS): Data on the mathematics and science achievement of our students compared to that of students in other countries.

CHAPTER 3
WHAT IS A DRIVING QUESTION?

Chapter Overview

This is the first of several chapters that focus on individual features of project-based science. Like all project-based science features, the driving question is based on ideas about how children learn science (see Chapter 2). The driving question organizes and drives the diverse activities of a project. Like project-based science, all of the chapters in this book are also organized by questions. These questions give the reader a focus and organize the ideas and activities in each chapter.

This chapter begins by answering, *What is a driving question*? The key features of a good driving question are feasibility, worth, contextualization, meaning, ethics, and sustainability. Each of these features make driving questions different from topic-focused questions. Developing good driving questions is not easy. Teachers can use a variety of strategies and sources to generate driving questions. Some examples include using personal interests, current news stories, other teachers, published curricula, and the World Wide Web. It is also important for students to ask and refine their own questions. Brainstorming, small-group sharing and critiquing guided by the key features of driving questions, and justification of selected questions can guide students in this process. Good driving questions are valuable for engaging students in working toward solutions to real-world problems over an extended period of time.

Chapter Learning Performances

- Define driving question.

- Explain the features of a driving question.

- Create driving questions and defend why they are good driving questions.

- Describe how to help children generate driving questions

- Distinguish between driving questions and topic-based questions.

- Explain the value of using driving questions to teach science.

Lesson Ideas

What Is a Driving Question?

Portfolio Activity 3.1 *Comparing the Three Scenarios:* This is a good introduction to driving questions. One of the three scenarios described in the text supplies an example of a driving question, particularly in contrast to the other two scenarios.

If you have not already done so, you should develop a driving question for the class. Like teachers using driving questions in their classrooms, you can develop the driving question yourself or involve your students in developing the class driving question. One strategy is to have a driving question that you supply, such as *How do I plan for project-based science in my classroom?* Then, with your students, develop another driving question based on one or more science concepts. This science question can be used to focus class activities as students also explore features of project-based science. This begins with the development of the driving question. Keep in mind that the class's driving question should meet all of the criteria for a good driving question. This includes leading your students to explore science ideas at a level that is intriguing to them as adult learners.

Like a teacher attempting project-based science for the first time, you also may decide to supply a science driving question for your class. This way you will better be able to anticipate the concepts and investigations that your students will develop.

Project Example

One example of a science-based driving question appropriate for your students is *How can I predict if a boat will float?* To answer this question your students will explore concepts of equilibrium and center of gravity. Students will bring up ideas about density, displacement, mass, and pressure. Using standard science equipment and some guidance, your students can design several investigations to answer this driving question.

> **Tip:** Many adults believe they know how to explain why a boat floats. However, when examined closely their ideas are inconsistent with scientific explanations.

This project will be used as an example throughout this manual. Details of investigation ideas and other lessons related to this question will be described in later chapters. Ideas for some activities included in this example project were adapted from Science & Technology for Children's (STC) kit *Floating and Sinking*. Other project-based science units that could be adapted for your students can be found at the hi-ce Web site: http://hi-ce.org

Portfolio Activity 3.2 *Comparing the Scenarios Again:* Students can complete this activity after a class discussion of the key features. Examples from the text, students' ideas, and questions from other sources such as published materials should be included in the discussion.

How Does the Driving Question Differ from Other Questions?

One way to help your students see the difference between driving questions and other types of questions is to explore in depth an example within a project. As students attempt to answer the driving question, they will begin to see how this question is different from the more familiar topic-based questions.

> **Tip:** Your students may have difficulty distinguishing topic-based questions from driving questions until they begin developing their own driving questions.

Project Example

To introduce the driving question *How can I predict if my boat will float?*, begin with a story or example of a boat floating or sinking. One story is found in the STC guide for *Floating and Sinking*. This story describes the need for a way to ensure that boats and ships are not overloaded and in danger of sinking. Your students can then share their own boat stories. This activity illustrates how a driving question can be connected to students' lives outside of school.

Next you can have your students do a KWL lesson. The KWL strategy is described in detail in Chapter 7, *How Do I Develop and Use Benchmark Lessons?* What do we <u>k</u>now about floating or sinking? How do we know these things (evidence)? What would we <u>w</u>ant or need to know to predict if a boat will float? This will demonstrate the KWL strategy in context. It will also demonstrate how a driving question is different from a topic question. Here all of the ideas are connected by the driving question rather than a series of distinct topics.

> **Tip:** Your students may not have experienced some of the example activities mentioned in the text. Stream tables and KWL are examples. You will want to explore these activities during class.

Portfolio Activity 3.3 *Evaluating Various Questions:* Once your students are familiar with the key features of driving questions, they can examine a variety of questions to evaluate whether they meet each of the criteria.

> <u>Visual Resources:</u> Table 3.1 Key Features of Driving Questions, available in the Instructor's area of the Online Learning Center.

You can extend this portfolio activity by asking students to browse back issues of *Science and Children* and *Science Scope* for examples of teacher-developed ideas that start with a question. They can evaluate these questions for use as driving questions for a project and make suggestions for how the questions could be modified to contain more of the features of a driving question.

How Is a Driving Question Developed?

Portfolio Activity 3.4 *Generating Driving Questions from Topics:* Have student work in small groups to develop driving questions for the given topics. Groups then can share their ideas with the class. This activity will prepare students for writing driving questions for their own topics.

You can extend this portfolio activity by asking students to bring in newspapers and magazines with articles on current topics in science. Students can work in groups to develop possible driving questions to focus on these current topics. They can trade questions with another group who will evaluate each question using the features of a good driving question. Make sure evaluators include both positive and "room for improvement" comments.

Portfolio Activity 3.5 *Analyze Classroom Science and Develop Driving Questions*

Have your students develop their own driving questions. By writing, sharing, and critiquing questions, students will develop a better understanding of good driving questions. Support your students in developing their own driving questions based on ideas from activities and lessons experienced in methods or other courses. First, have students choose a topic that aligns with a benchmark or standards. Then they can begin looking for resources to use for materials and ideas. When possible, have your students select concepts that they will teach sometime in the future. In-service teachers can develop questions for concepts that are a part of their school curriculum. Likewise, student teachers can develop questions based on concepts they will teach during field or student teaching experiences.

Developing a driving question is more difficult than it appears. Few initial driving questions will match all of the key features of driving questions. Give your students the opportunity to share, revise, and improve their driving questions. Also, revisit the driving questions in later chapters when developing investigations or benchmark lessons.

> **Tip:** Revising work may be a new idea to many students. You may need to support them in using class feedback to improve their work.

Guide your students in selecting benchmarks and standards to be addressed by their driving questions. Students are often too broad in their selection, choosing all benchmarks even remotely related to the question rather than those explicitly addressed by lessons. Other students will not recognize matching standards if the wording is not matched to their ideas of the concept.

Portfolio Activity 3.6 *Developing Driving Questions from What Students Know:* Your students can incorporate what they learn about children's ideas into the development of their driving questions. This is particularly useful if your students will have the opportunity to teach their projects.

> **Tip:** Reinforce the idea that teachers guide students in developing good driving questions. Also, students' questions can be incorporated as sub-questions or investigation questions.

Developing a driving question is a good place to begin supporting your students in collaboration, even though this is a topic of a later chapter. Brainstorming, sharing ideas, and critiquing questions is a valuable opportunity to model collaboration strategies. This activity will be one example for your students to reflect on when collaboration is the topic, in Chapter 6.

> <u>Visual Resources:</u> Figure 3.2 Brainstorming Wheel, available in the Instructor's area of the Online Learning Center.

What Is the Value of the Driving Question?

Project Example

As the project progresses, your students will see you using the class driving question to connect your lessons and activities. You are modeling the use of the driving question. You will want to revisit the use of driving questions again as students develop investigations and artifacts for this project.

One appropriate artifact for this project is to design a boat to float. You should tell your students that they will need to be able to explain how their design will ensure their boat is not in danger of sinking. You will give them the details of this task as the project progresses. Student assessment using this artifact will be discussed in Chapters 8 and 9.

Many college students do not recognize the depth of understanding intended by benchmarks and standards. In addition, some students will not understand the science concepts themselves. Lessons that give your students opportunities to explore and construct their own understanding of the science content will also help them to understand the value of driving questions and project-based science.

How Can a Driving Question Be Used Throughout a Project?

Revisit the driving question of this chapter, *What is a driving question?* Have we answered this question? What did we do that helped to answer this question? What about the driving question for the course, *How do I plan for project-based science in my classroom?* What do we now know? What do we not know? Use this discussion to lead students to the next question for Chapter 4.

> **Tip:** Students frequently forget to connect ideas from each lesson to the driving question. Often this connection is done only at the end of the project. This does not take advantage of the driving question as an instructional tool.

<u>Discussion Questions</u>

How do you know when it is appropriate for the teacher to develop a driving question and when is it appropriate for students? What are the advantages and disadvantages in each case?

If traditional science textbooks are organized around topics rather than driving questions, what is the value of a textbook in a project-based science classroom? In what ways could you use a traditional textbook in a project-based science classroom?

Many teachers assign science fair projects for students to work on independently during the year. There are many books and other resources listing ideas for possible topics for children to explore in a science fair project. Discuss how the titles of these kinds of projects compare and contrast with driving questions in project-based science. (Note: You might obtain some titles from books on science fair projects, or from the Westinghouse Talent Search Competition booklets of titles of science fair projects.)

Discuss the various strategies you could use to keep your students focused on the driving question. Are some of these strategies more appropriate for younger students than for older students? In what ways can you connect the activities and benchmark lessons to the driving question throughout the project?

Assessment Ideas

Portfolio Assessment

One assessment idea is to require specific portfolio activities to be included in students' portfolios. This can be a formative assessment giving you information about your students' developing understanding as they participate in class activities and discussions. Reading portfolio responses also allows you to read what each student is thinking, not just those who speak up in class. Portfolio Activities 3.2, *Comparing the Three Scenarios Again*, and 3.3, *Evaluating Various Questions*, are particularly useful for formative assessment. Activity 3.2 targets understanding of the key features. Activity 3.3 evaluates good and poor driving questions. Both of these activities lead into the next two assessment ideas.

Question Evaluation

Another assessment strategy is to have students write descriptions of their own driving questions. Tell your students to describe how each feature of a good driving question is reflected in their questions. Because writing a good driving question is very difficult, particularly for novices, their questions may not meet all of the six criteria. However, your students can describe how their questions compare to each criterion, including a description of how they think their questions need to be improved. This assessment strategy is appropriate for classes that have discussed various example questions and have shared their ideas about their own driving questions. Students' written descriptions will demonstrate their understanding of the criteria and their ability to apply the criteria to their driving question.

> **Tip:** Initially your students may not feel comfortable pointing out aspects of their work that need improvement. You should reassure them that you are interested in their application of the key features, not their ability to write an excellent driving question on their first try.

An alternative to the first assessment suggestion is to give students one or two sample questions to critique. You can include both good and poor driving questions. Students can use the key features to evaluate each question as good or poor and to explain why.

Driving Question Development

Finally, your students should develop a driving question for their own project plans. Students will need to revisit and revise their question as they learn about investigations, benchmark lessons, and other project-based science features in future chapters. Therefore, you should assess their driving questions at a later date. At that time you will be able to see how your students have used their driving questions to organize and drive their unit activities. In addition, if your students include their initial driving questions in their portfolios, both you and your students will be able to see their progress and how a driving question develops over time.

Resources

Text Resources

American Association for the Advancement of Science (1990). *Science for All Americans*. New York: Oxford University Press.

American Association for the Advancement of Science (1993). *Benchmarks for Science Literacy*. New York: Oxford University Press.

Beck, T. A. (1998). Are there any questions? One teacher's view of students and their questions in a fourth-grade classroom. *Teaching and Teacher Education*, 14(8): 871–886.

Marx, R. W., Blumenfeld, P. C., Krajcik, J. S., and Soloway, E. (1997). Enacting project-based science. *Elementary School Journal*, 97(4): 341–358.

National Research Council (1996). *National Science Education Standards*. Washington, D.C.: National Academy Press.

Rosenshine, B., Meister, C., and Chapman, S. (1996). Teaching students to generate questions: A review of the intervention studies. *Review of Educational Research*, 66: 181–221.

Science & Technology for Children (STC). (2002). *Floating and Sinking*. Available from Carolina, http://www.carolina.com/STC/index.asp

Internet Resources

You can access all of these sites directly on the Instructor's area of the Online Learning Center. Web addresses will be updated there as changes are made.

Bellingham School District online research investigations (http://www.bham.wednet.edu/online.htm): Examples of student research projects tied to the science and social studies curriculum.

CoVis project at Northwestern University (http://www.covis.nwu.edu/): Through the use of advanced technologies, the CoVis Project is attempts to transform science learning to better resemble the authentic question-centered, collaborative practice of real scientists.

Eisenhower National Clearinghouse for Mathematics and Science Education (http://www.enc.org): Source of ideas and examples of question-centered research projects.

Enemy or ally? Friend or foe? (http://sln.fi.edu/tfi/units/energy/wind.html): Provides idea of exploring aspects of wind energy; includes reports from schools that have used the project.

GLOBE project (http://www.globe.gov): GLOBE is a worldwide, hands-on, primary and secondary school-based science and education program. GLOBE provides students the opportunity to learn by collecting data, mapping, and sharing ideas through the Internet related to atmosphere, hydrology, soils, and land cover/phenology.

Highly Interactive Computing in Education, hi-ce (http://hi-ce.org): Source of project-based, technology-enhanced middle school curriculum materials developed to answer a driving question.

Learning Technologies in Urban Schools, LeTUS (http://www.letus.org): Source of project-based, technology-enhanced middle school curriculum materials developed to answer a driving question.

National Science Teachers Association (http://www.nsta.org): Information on the most recent ideas in teaching science to children, including on-line journals *Science and Children* and *Science Scope*; on-line store for real-world problem-based instructional materials for teachers.

Web-Based Inquiry Science Environment (http://wise.berkeley.edu/welcome.php): Technology to create driving questions.

Tom Snyder Productions (http://www.tomsnyder.com): Science Seekers, a collection of CD-ROM-based materials designed to engage elementary and middle school students in solving today's real-world problems with science.

CHAPTER 4
HOW ARE SCIENTIFIC INVESTIGATIONS DEVELOPED?

Chapter Overview

This chapter describes the central importance of investigations to science and the central role teachers play in helping students design and plan investigations. The various components of scientific investigations include refining questions, planning and designing experiments, assembling and carrying out procedures, analyzing data, and sharing information with others. Children at different ages are capable of doing various parts of investigations. Teachers play an important role in helping students engage in investigations.

An investigation web can help students structure their own investigations. The various parts of the investigation web include messing about, finding information, asking and refining questions, planning and designing, conducting the investigation, making sense of data, and sharing ideas. The investigation web highlights the interconnection of each component and the iterative nature of investigation. There are many strategies teachers can use to support children in carrying out parts of the investigation web. These include modeling an investigation, offering structure for each component, and providing feedback. Teachers can evaluate investigations to determine whether students are doing the cognitive work rather than having science done for them.

Chapter Learning Performances

- Explain the value of elementary and middle grade students engaging in investigations.

- Clarify the components of the investigative web.

- Design and carry out investigations with students.

- Critique and give feedback to elementary and middle grade students on the various components of an investigation

- Judge the quality of opportunities for students engaging in investigations.

Lesson Ideas

> **Tip:** Your students will need time to explore all of the components of investigations and to learn how to plan investigations for their students. In addition, other features of project-based science such as technology tools and collaboration can be incorporated in the discussion of investigations. Your students will understand topics of future chapters more quickly having first experienced the topic within this chapter on investigations.

Investigations in Elementary and Middle School Science Instruction

A good way to begin is to find out what your students know about science investigations and what they think students should do during investigations. One way to do this is to have your students reflect on and write a description of a science investigation they can remember doing. Some questions to guide their writing include the following: What was it like? What was the purpose? Did you enjoy it? Did you understand it? What did you learn?

Then you can ask your students to write a short description of what they would have their students do during an investigation. What will their students do? Why? In which ways will it be the same as or different from the investigation you remember? Why?

> **Tip:** Your students will have many ideas about science investigations and students. However, many of their ideas will be based on their experiences as students in secondary or college-level science courses. For most students this will mean they remember short, one-session experiments that were often verification lab exercises.

Have several students share their investigation memories and plans. You and your students should revisit their initial ideas at the end of the chapter to see what ideas have changed.

The Investigation Web

McComas' article *15 myths of science* is an interesting description of science versus what many people believe about science. Reading and discussing this article together in class is a good way to introduce students to the investigation web.

> **Tip:** Many of your students will be familiar with the "scientific method," a list of six or more steps to be performed in order. Typically these steps match the components of a written experiment report rather than methods used by scientists to answer scientific questions.

> <u>Visual Resources</u>: Figure 4.1 The Investigation Web, available in the Instructor's area of the Online Learning Center.

The best way to help your students understand investigations and how investigations support student learning is to have them participate in an extended investigation. This investigation should be connected to answering a driving question, preferably the driving question established in Chapter 3. If you began with the project example introduced in Chapter 3, you can continue with each component described here in Chapter 4. If you and your class chose another science topic and driving question, you can adapt the project example to conduct an investigation to match your class's driving question.

Other ideas for long-term, student-designed investigations include (1) investigating various environmental factors that affect the growth of plants such as acid rain, detergents, light, temperature, and salt from roads; (2) studying the factors that affect the behavior of sowbugs; (3) investigating conditions that prevent bread from molding; (4) investigating what kinds of food different birds prefer at a feeder; (5) investigating how different exercises affect your heart rate; or (6) designing the best insulated structure that keeps an ice cube from melting. A good source of investigations appropriate for elementary and middle school students is Julia Cothron et al., *Science Experiments by the Hundreds*.

> **Tip:** It is easy for teachers to get the idea that all traditional activities are bad instruction. Although these activities are not true investigations, they can be valuable learning experiences. One type of non-investigative lesson is the benchmark lesson discussed in Chapter 7.

Portfolio Activities 4.1 through 4.7 in this section address individual components of the investigation process. You can incorporate these portfolio activities as part of the class's investigation. One way to this is to replace the specific content of the portfolio activity with that of the class project example. For example, Portfolio Activity 4.4, *Writing Procedures*, uses a general procedure-writing task with Legos. Instead, your students could write procedures for their investigations. Alternatively, you could have the class complete each of the portfolio activities as written and add your class's investigation to the activity. For example, Portfolio Activity 4.2, *Identifying Testable Questions*, examines several questions to identify those that are testable. Your class can add their own questions to the list to be evaluated and revised.

All of the strategies described in the text to support student investigations will also be helpful for your students. You can support your students in conducting investigations with these same strategies. Your students will revisit these strategies when they begin to plan an investigation for students as part of their project plans.

> **Tip:** Some teachers believe that real investigations are too complex or difficult for most students, particularly in early grades. Students can do their own investigations, but they need to be guided through the process. Point out the strategies you used to help your class with their first investigation.

Project Example

One component of the investigation web is messing about or exploring the ideas and materials. Before your students will be able to design their own investigations to answer *How can I predict if my boat will float?*, they will need to explore some of the factors they might need to investigate and the available materials. Using small tubs of water, students can work in groups to purposefully explore what factors are associated with floating. For example, a common idea is that heavy things sink. Students can test some heavy and light objects such as large and small blocks of wood and large and small blocks of lead or other dense material. The heavy large wooden block floats and the lighter small lead block sinks. This illustrates that although weight is a factor, it is not the only factor. Other factors to explore include size, shape, and type of material.

As described in the text, you will need to guide your students' exploration so that it is purposeful yet open. Although they can choose the factors they test, they should think about why that factor would make the object float or sink. They can also connect each factor back to their initial ideas about floating. You can guide their thinking by asking questions such as, What does weight feel like? When you hold a heavy object, what do you feel? In what direction does the weight push? You also can include some tests that everyone must do. One example is to have your students cut out pieces of wax paper the size of their hands and float them on the water. Then, with an open hand, students push on the wax paper. Again ask, What do you feel? In what direction do you feel the push? Your students should also push on other floating objects to feel the buoyant force. Together these examples bring in the ideas of forces, direction, and floating. At the end of the exploration your students should have some ideas about factors that would make good investigation questions.

Portfolio Activity 4.1 *Going on a Stream Walk:* This activity is an example of a purposeful initial observation.

> **Tip:** The text describes the use of mystery boxes to help students improve their observation skills. You might make a set of mystery boxes for your students to examine.

Portfolio Activity 4.2 *Identifying Testable Questions*: Have your students add their own questions to this list, including questions from their project examples they are investigating in class.

Project Example

Have your students develop questions based on their observations from their exploration of factors related to floating and sinking. Students can brainstorm questions as a whole class or in groups and then share questions with the class. Next, have your students identify each question as testable or not. If not, how should the question be revised? Then each student group can choose a question they would like to investigate. They can write a hypothesis for this question and share their hypothesis with the class. Finally, students can reflect on their questions and hypotheses. How are these questions similar or different from what children would ask? How would the process of writing hypotheses be different for children?

Portfolio Activity 4.3 *Making Hypotheses from Questions:* Again, Have your students add their own questions to this list, including questions from the project examples they are investigating in class.

> **Tip:** It is a common misconception that students cannot write an incorrect hypothesis because it is a guess about what will happen. Although writing a hypothesis that will not be supported by the investigation evidence can be appropriate, writing a hypothesis that does not guide the collection of data or connect to science ideas is not. In the latter case, the hypothesis is incorrectly constructed and should be rewritten.

Project Example

Here is an excellent opportunity to introduce the use of educational technology. In the project example your students are exploring boat designs. One place to find information about boats and other objects that sink or float is on the World Wide Web. Artemis is a tool that supports students in exploring the Web. Artemis as well as many other educational technology tools is described in Chapter 5. By having students use this tool here to support their investigation of boat design, they can see first-hand how technology can support learning.

> Visual Resources: Table 3.1 Central Ideas, available in the Instructor's area of the Online Learning Center.

Portfolio Activity 4.4 *Writing Procedures:* Your students can write procedures for the investigations they are doing as part of the project example.

Project Example

For this first investigation it may be a good idea to have all student groups investigate the same variable. One choice is to investigate the relationship between buoyant force and size of the object. Students will have noticed that larger floating objects are more difficult to push under the water or sink. In this investigation students would collect data or evidence to support their ideas about this relationship. Because the investigation is relatively simple, students can concentrate on the components of the investigation process.

You will need to show the class how to measure buoyant force. One simple way to measure buoyant force is described in the teacher's manual for Science & Technology for Children's *Floating and Sinking*. This method uses a suction cup with an attached hook like the type used to decorate windows. Stick the suction cup to the bottom of the tub of water. Then simply run a string attached to the floating object down through the hook and back up. Attach a spring scale to the other end and pull. The force of the water pushing up on the object can be read from the spring scale in your hand. Fishing bobbers in several sizes make excellent floating objects for this investigation.

Portfolio Activity 4.5 *Controlling Variables: Paper Dragon Races*

Portfolio Activity 4.6 *Sprouting Bean Plants*: This activity is a good one to do in class. It is also an appropriate activity for your students to keep in their portfolios for assessment.

Portfolio Activity 4.7 *Planning and Designing*

Project Example

In the investigation described above, students will collect similar data. However, if you do not give the class step-by-step procedures to follow, chances are some groups will do the investigation slightly differently. This is actually a good opportunity to discuss why and how to control variables. When students share their data and find groups are reporting different values, a discussion about controlling variables will be very meaningful. To ensure that some groups will have different data, you can set up some of the tubs with salt water and others with fresh water. This variable will change the measure of buoyant force even if all other variables are controlled. When your students discover the discrepancies between each group's data they may decide they want to repeat the investigation. This time they may want to have a class decision on how to measure the variables and collect the data.

> **Tip:** Your students may get very involved in the investigation when they find everyone has different data. Discussing, revising, and redoing the investigation is an excellent illustration of collaboration as well as investigation.

If your students are unaware of the salty versus fresh water variable, they will first work to eliminate all other possible explanations for the different measurements. They will then need to examine their assumptions, including the assumption that all the tubs of water were the same. This can be an interesting discussion of the nature of science and the influence of underlying assumptions.

Supporting Students' Implementation of Investigations

Portfolio Activity 4.8 *Performing Your Own Investigation:* This activity is perfect for structuring your students' investigation in the project example. If this is their second investigation, you can let each group chose its own questions and design following the guidelines given here. This activity is also an excellent component to include as a portfolio assessment.

Project Example

Have your students design and conduct a second investigation. Each group can choose its own question based on what the class has already learned and what is yet not explained. Revisiting the driving question and the list of student-generated questions is a good way to help your students develop their own investigation questions. Remind your students that they will use what they learn in their investigations to design their own boats that will float.

> **Tip:** You will need to model appropriate ways to critique or disagree with data presented by your students. Be careful to focus on the data and analysis, not students' abilities. You should also tell the class what you are doing and then have students take over the role of critic in the discussion.

Make sure your students share their ideas at several stages, including a presentation of their findings and conclusions. They should discuss their evidence for their ideas about what factors influence floating. Because they are doing this project example on their own level, your students will bring in more ideas and will work through these ideas more quickly than children will. These class discussions should include a reflection on how investigations supported their own learning and what would be different with children. This will help your students make the transition to begin planning an investigation lesson for students.

> **Tip:** Teachers should provide many supports for students to do their own investigations. Teachers should not, however, structure activities so tightly that students do not need to do cognitive work. This distinction may not be an easy one for your students to make.

Portfolio Activity 4.9 *Supporting Implementation of Investigations*

Investigation Development

Have your students develop a plan for an investigation they would use with students. You will need to give your students some guidelines or structure for what they should include in their plans. For example, investigation plans should include strategies to keep students focused on the science ideas. Encourage your students to use the many tables and strategies described in the text in their own investigation plans. You also will want your students to share their investigation plans with the class. A discussion of positive features and suggestions for improvement can be great learning experience for everyone. Students can then incorporate feedback from you and the class into their revised plans.

> **Tip:** Purposeful use of published materials can be an important resource for teachers. However, many teachers believe they should follow their students' science textbook closely. Alternatively, some teachers believe they should not use textbook materials at all—that to do so is a sign of poor teaching. Support your students in learning how to adapt materials to meet their students' learning needs.

Criteria for Assessing the Value of an Investigation

Portfolio Activity 4.10 *Comparing Two Investigations:* Use Table 4.16, *Reflecting on the Structure of an Investigation*, to evaluate Portfolio Activity 4.10, the project example, and then their own investigation.

Visual Resources: Table 3.1 Reflecting on the Structure of an Investigation, available in the Instructor's area of the Online Learning Center.

Investigation Evaluation

Now that everyone has seen several examples of investigations, including at least one extended investigation completed in class, it is a good time to revisit each example. Have students compare each of the examples to traditional experiments and hands-on activities. Also, have your students look at the national standards for inquiry. How did each activity address the standards for inquiry?

> **Tip:** Highlight that good investigations include helping students develop inquiry skills and content understanding at the same time.

Have your students read over their initial ideas about science investigation written at the beginning of this chapter. Have any ideas changed? If so, how are they different? Are any ideas still the same? How will their ideas impact what they will do in the classroom?

Tip: Your students may not recognize their own practices as traditional. This may be because they do not yet understand inquiry and cannot distinguish true inquiry from hands-on activities. Sharing their lesson ideas and other examples can help student see the difference.

Discussion Questions

Imagine that you wanted to teach your students about sound. You decide to have them explore musical instruments. Discuss what kinds of investigations using musical instruments would be appropriate for different-level students: children ages 5–7; children ages 6–9; children 8–12; and children 11–13.

Do all scientists follow the scientific method? How is using the investigation web like what scientists do in the "real world"? Do all scientists start with asking a question? How is what your students do in school different from what scientists do? What is science? Compare your ideas of scientific investigations with the ideas presented in Chapter 1 of *Science for All Americans*.

In what ways can a teacher support students in designing their own investigations? What strategies would be important to use? What kinds of resources would be useful?

Conduct a class discussion about a scientific discovery reported in a recent newspaper or science magazine. What kind of evidence did the scientist provide for the conclusions? What questions do you have about how the research was conducted? What about the findings? Are they valid? Are they reliable?

Assessment Ideas

Portfolio Assessment

This chapter contains suggested portfolio activities for each component of investigations. You may decide to include only a purposefully chosen selection of activities to be included in your students' portfolios or that you will use for assessment. Portfolio Activities 4.6, *Sprouting Bean Plants*, 4.8, *Performing Your Own Investigation*, and 4.10, *Comparing Two Investigations* are particularly useful for formative assessment. Activity 4.6 targets understanding of investigation design and planning. Activity 4.8 guides students through each of the components of their own investigation. Activity 4.10 evaluates good and poor investigations. Each of these activities leads into the following assessment ideas.

Investigation Example

The investigations your students completed can be assessed for their ability to do each component. For example, you can evaluate each student's hypothesis, design, analysis, or conclusions. These can be evaluated for process (e.g., was the hypothesis appropriate to guide data collection?) or for content (e.g., does the conclusion show understanding of the science content?). Alternatively, you can ask students to describe how each component of the investigation web was represented in their work and how it contributed to their understanding of investigations and the intended science content.

Investigation Evaluation

Students can use Table 4.16, *Reflecting on the Structure of an Investigation*, to evaluate one or more investigation lessons. These lessons can include examples from their experience, published curriculum materials, or their own investigation lesson plans. Students should describe how each factor is met or is not met. This will demonstrate their understanding of factors that distinguish investigations from other hands-on activities.

Investigation Development

In a continuation of their project planning, students should develop an investigation lesson that addresses science ideas related to their unit's driving question. This investigation should include some of the suggested strategies described in the text adapted for their specific lesson. Also, this investigation lesson is not necessarily a one-class-period lesson. Rather, it should be an extended lesson spanning multiple class periods. Finally, students should write a rationale statement describing how their lesson supports students in doing their own investigation and in understanding the science ideas.

Resources

Text Resources

American Association for the Advancement of Science (1990). *Science for All Americans*. New York: Oxford University Press.

American Association for the Advancement of Science (1993). *Benchmarks for Science Literacy*. New York: Oxford University Press.

Cothron, J. Giese, R., and Rezba, R. (1996). *Science Experiments by the Hundreds*. Dubuque, IA: Kendall Hunt Publishing Co.

Ingram, M. (1993). *Bottle Biology*. Dubuque, IA: Kendall/Hunt Publishing Company.

Krajcik, J. S. (1993). Learning science by doing science. In R. E. Yager (Ed.), *What Research Says to the Science Teacher: Science, Society and Technology* (Vol. 7, pp. 53–58). Washington, D.C.: National Science Teachers Association.

Krajcik, J. S., Blumenfeld, P. C., Marx, R. W., Bass, C. M., and Fredricks, J. (1998). Inquiry in project-based science classrooms: Initial attempts by middle school students. *The Journal of the Learning Sciences*, 7(3&4): 313–350.

Krajcik, J. S., Blumenfeld, P. C., Marx, R. W., and Soloway, E. (1999). Instructional, curricular, and technological supports for inquiry in science classrooms. In J. Minstrell and E. V. Zee (Eds.), *Inquiry into Inquiry Science Learning and Teaching*. Washington, D.C.: American Association for the Advancement of Science Press.

Kuhn, D. (1989). Children and adults as intuitive scientists. *Psychological Review*, 96(4): 674–689.

Layman, J. W. (1996). *Inquiry and Learning: Realizing Science Standards in the Classroom*. New York: The College Board.

Lawrence Hall of Science (2000). *Full Option Science System (FOSS)*. Nashua, NH: Delta Education.

Lunetta, V. N. (1998). The school science laboratory: Historical perspectives and contexts for contemporary teaching. In B. J. Fraser and K. G. Tobin (Eds.), *International Handbook of Science Education*. (Vol. 1, pp. 249–264). Dordrecht, The Netherlands: Kluwer Academic Publishers.

McComas, W. F. (1997). 15 myths of science. *Skeptic*, 5(2): 88–95.

National Research Council (1996). *National Science Education Standards*. Washington, D.C.: National Academy Press.

Science & Technology for Children (STC). (2002). *Floating and Sinking*. Available from Carolina, http://www.carolina.com/STC/index.asp

Internet Resources

You can access all of these sites directly on the Instructor's area of the Online Learning Center. Web addresses will be updated there as changes are made.

Artemis (http://webartemis.org): On-line collection specifically designed for middle and high school students. The Web resources within the digital library have been preselected by librarians, keeping in mind the learning needs and reading levels of students.

Elementary Science Olympiad (http://garnet.acns.fsu.edu/~ddp0223/classroom.html): Links to descriptions of inquiry-based activities; offers more than 80 challenging and motivational events that are balanced among the various science disciplines of life science, earth science, and physical science. Individual and team events require knowledge of science facts, concepts, process skills, and applications.

Exploratorium Institute for Inquiry (http://www.exploratorium.edu/IFI/index.html): San Francisco Exploratorium Museum page focusing on inquiry-based professional development activities; linked to other inquiry resource pages.

Highly Interactive Computing in Education hi-ce (http://hi-ce.org): Source of project-based, technology-enhanced middle school curriculum materials emphasizing student investigations.

Lawrence Hall of Science (http://www.lhs.berkeley.edu): Publications and other products to encourage student science exploration. Full option science system FOSS kits.

Lawrence Hall of Science SAVI/SELPH (http://www.lhs.berkeley.edu/FOSS/SAVI_SELPH.html) Science Activities for the Visually Impaired/Science Enrichment for Learners with Physical Handicaps.

Learning Technologies in Urban Schools LeTUS (http://www.letus.org): Source of project-based, technology-enhanced middle school curriculum materials emphasizing student investigations.

National Academy of Science (http://www.nas.edu) Includes links to entire on-line text of *The National Science Education Standards*; describes what elementary and middle level students should know *about* scientific inquiry and how to *do* inquiry.

National Gardening (http://www.kidsgardening.com/teachers.asp#new): More than 100 science inquiry investigations and experiments related to plants; *It's all in the eyes: Inquiry up close*, a three-part video series about two teachers' experience with inquiry in a kindergarten and middle school classroom focused on growing potatoes, is available through their catalog.

National Science Education Standards (http://www.nap.edu/books/0309053269/html): Includes specific standards for student understanding of inquiry.

SciLinks (http://www.nsta.org/scilinks): SciLinks is an exciting partnership between progressive U.S. textbook publishers and NSTA, the largest organization of science educators in the world. If your textbook has SciLinks, you and your students will have the best Internet science sources at your fingertips all preselected and preapproved by NSTA's network of teacher–Webwatchers.

Skepticism (www.youngskeptics.org): The Young Skeptics Program aims to develop and foster an understanding of the world through inquiry-based learning. They provide material to complement and enhance existing science and educational programs.

Sowbugs (http://ohioline.osu.edu/hyg-fact/2000/2072.html): Ohio State University Extension Fact Sheet; information to support investigations with sowbugs (pillbugs).

CHAPTER 5
HOW CAN LEARNING TECHNOLOGIES BE USED TO SUPPORT INVESTIGATIONS?

Chapter Overview

Learning technologies are an important resource for teachers to help them support students in developing meaningful understandings of science concepts and in doing investigations. Learning technologies include computers, software, and various peripherals that support student learning. Learning technologies can help students actively engage with phenomena, use and apply knowledge, find new sources of information, create multiple representations of learning, and create learning communities. Technology can play a powerful role in enhancing student and teacher motivation by actively engaging students in the learning process.

This chapter describes many wonderful examples of technology tools that can support students in science. Each type of learning technology offers students and teachers unique benefits. Microcomputer-based laboratories allow students to collect, visualize, and analyze data. Simulations, microworlds, and interactive multimedia allow students to explore phenomena when it is unsafe, too expensive, impractical, or perhaps even unethical for students to have first-hand experiences. The World Wide Web offers the advantage of access to the newest information and data. However, the Web also brings challenges such as the high number of sites returned when students conduct a search. Digital libraries can help by providing preselected and preapproved sites. Technology can help students create multimedia documents to represent what they know in a variety of forms. Telecommunications, including email, threaded discussions, and chat rooms, allows students access to a wider community.

Learning technologies can offer many advantages for instruction in science but should not be used for the sake of using technology. Teachers should use technology when it can help students meet important instructional learning outcomes or develop meaningful understandings. It is the responsibility of the teacher to make decisions regarding when and how to best use learning technologies in the science classroom.

Chapter Learning Performances

- Describe how students can use new learning technologies to support them in carrying out investigations.

- Compare and contrast the various ways in which children can use technology to develop meaningful understandings.

- Use new technology tools to explore scientific ideas.

- Explain what to take into consideration when designing instruction using new learning technologies.

- Explain how learning technologies can extend the boundaries of the classroom.

- Discuss some of the pitfalls of using technology in the classroom.

Lesson Ideas

The Role of Technology in Constructing Science Understandings

A good way to start this chapter on learning technology is to find out what experiences and ideas your students have regarding technology tools. Portfolio Activities 5.1 and 5.2 are good activities to begin a discussion about their experiences using technology for learning and their ideas about children using technology tools.

> **Tip:** When teachers anticipate they will have limited access to computers or other technology resources, they may have difficulty seeing a purpose in learning about technology tools. This is often the case for teachers who are planning to or are already teaching in urban settings. You will want to address their reluctance by exploring strategies for overcoming limited access and highlighting the benefits of learning technologies for urban students.

Portfolio Activity 5.1 *Ways in Which You Have Used Technologies for Learning*

Portfolio Activity 5.2 *Why Should Children Use Learning Technology?*

Have your students share their experiences and ideas about learning technologies in small groups or whole-class discussion. Listen for ideas or experiences that you will need to address during this chapter.

> **Tip:** If you have used any technology tools during earlier chapters, you may already have some ideas about your students' computer skills. It is still important to explicitly explore their ideas and experiences here, as your students will be exploring a wide variety of learning technologies.

This discussion is an opportunity for you to identify those students who will need more support in learning basic computer skills. One strategy to help these students is to arrange heterogeneous groups. Students with more computer experience can guide novices in learning basic skills.

> **Tip:** Some teachers are reluctant to use learning technology and may become frustrated during technology-based activities because they are uncomfortable using technology themselves. These same teachers will be excited about using technology after they develop basic skills and see what students can do with these tools.

Technology-Enhanced Lesson Examples

Plan to have your students spend time learning at least one or two technology tools in depth. Then they can explore many other examples more quickly. Portfolio Activities 5.3 and 5.5 through 5.9 lead students in exploring a variety of innovative learning technologies. Because most students will have questions while they are using these tools, you will need to allot time during class for each of these portfolio activities. Together these activities will give your students an idea of the range of possibilities. Later, when your students are planning their own technology-based lessons, they can revisit these examples.

> **Tip:** Many of the learning technologies described in this chapter will be new to your students. You will want to allow ample time for them to learn about and with technology.

Project Example

Include the use of one or more of the example learning technologies as part of an extended inquiry into a driving question. If you are using the project example *How can I predict if a boat will float?*, you can use Artemis as described in Portfolio Activity 5.8 to search for information on boat design. You can also incorporate the use of multimedia documents to illustrate ideas about how to design a boat that floats.

Another example is to use temperature, pH, and dissolved oxygen sensors to investigate water quality as part of a project such as *What is the quality of the water in the stream by my school?* This investigation can be incorporated into the previous chapter on investigations.

Portfolio Activity 5.3 *Using Microcomputer-Based Laboratories to Visualize Evaporative Cooling:* Your students could also use motion sensors to visualize motions of different speeds and directions. Motion sensors can also be used to investigate variable that influence the motion of a cart down a ramp.

Portfolio Activity 5.4 *The Value of Using Microcomputer-Based Laboratories in the Classroom*

Portfolio Activity 5.5 *Using the World Wide Web to Access and Visualize Data: Exploring the FeederWatch Program*

Portfolio Activity 5.6 *The Value of Using Simulations to Help Students Learn Science Concepts*

> **Tip:** Emphasize that learning technologies such as simulations should not be used to replace experiences with phenomena that are safe and doable for students.

Portfolio Activity 5.7 *The Value of Building Models for Helping Students Learn Science Concepts*

> **Tip:** At first glance models may appear to be the same as concept maps to your students. However, models depict dynamic relationships between variables, whereas concept maps depict hierarchical relationships between concepts.

> Visual Resources: Table 5.2 Advantages of the World Wide Web for Supporting Inquiry, available in the Instructor's area of the Online Learning Center.

Portfolio Activity 5.8 *The Value of Searching for Materials on the World Wide Web Using Digital Libraries*

> **Tip:** It is easy for teachers to get the idea that students should use technology such as the Web for the sake of using it or in order to learn technology skills alone. Emphasize the importance of selecting a tool to meet students' learning needs and science content objectives.

Portfolio Activity 5.9 *The Value of Creating Multimedia Documents:* Your students can create multimedia documents as part of their project examples about boat design or another topic. Have your students save these documents as example artifacts for the discussion of assessment in Chapter 9.

> **Tip:** Your students, like children, will be interested in exploring color, font, sound, and picture functions of the software. Encourage them to incorporate science ideas into their multimedia documents.

Role of the Teacher

Now that your students have first-hand experience with several learning technologies, it is a good time to stop and discuss the learning benefits and challenges of using technology tools in the classroom. Your students can reflect on each example lesson. Have your students focus on the following discussion questions:

- How was the lesson structured?

- What knowledge or skills were required before using the technology?

- What knowledge or skills were required during the use of technology? How were you supported in using the technology?

- What could students learn with the technology that would be more difficult or impossible without the tool?

- What were the pitfalls or challenges associated with using the tool? What could a teacher do to avoid or lessen these challenges?

- How should these technology-enhanced lessons be modified for students at different grade levels?

Finally, have your students revisit their initial ideas about learning technologies described in Portfolio Activities 5.1 and 5.2. What have they learned? Have any ideas changed? If so, how are they different? Are any ideas still the same? How will their ideas impact what they will do in the classroom? Discuss any initial concerns your students had about using technology in the classroom.

Integrating Technology into Instruction

Learning Technology Evaluation

Although many wonderful learning technologies are presented in the portfolio activities, many more are described in the text. References to countless more examples can be found on sites such as the Eisenhower National Clearinghouse. Your students will need to be able to select technology tools that meet the learning needs of their students. Have your students establish criteria for evaluating learning technology. They can begin with the list of issues to consider when incorporating technological tools into our curriculum described in the text. Then student groups should select a technology tool to evaluate and present to the class. You might decide to give each group parameters to guide their selection so that everyone is evaluating a different type of technology tool.

Portfolio Activity 5.10 *Using New Learning Technologies to Help Students Learn Science*

> **Tip:** Using technology can be interesting and fun for students. But motivation is not the only benefit for students. Emphasize that technology tools should be used for instruction because they can help students learn important science ideas.

Technology-Enhanced Lesson Development

Have your students select a learning technology to include in their project plans. They should focus on one technology tool and develop plans for one extended lesson using this tool. You will need to give your students a framework to use in their planning. In addition to generic lesson-plan components, your students should include components specific for the use of technology. One example is to have their lessons include four components: (1) pre-technology activities, (2) learning about the technology, (3) technology activities, and (4) post-technology activities. You will also want your students to share their investigation plans with the class. A discussion of positive features and suggestions for improvement can be great learning experience for everyone. Students can then incorporate feedback from you and the class into their revised plans.

Discussion Questions

Think of an idea or task that is difficult for students. What type of technology tool might help? What features would this tool have? Why? Explore some of the resources listed in this chapter to see if there is a technology tool like the one you describe.

Are there times when students should *not* use technology? Why?

What are some of the possible challenges of using technology with students? What could you do to address these challenges and make using learning technology a positive experience for both you and your students? For example, some applications use the Internet. However, Internet access at your school may be unreliable or unavailable. What can teachers do if their classes cannot access the Internet?

Using technology tools usually requires much planning and preparation on the part of teachers, not to mention expense and time for students to learn the tool itself. Why should teachers and students use learning technologies?

What factors should teachers consider when selecting and planning for technology?

You may find yourself teaching in a school district with limited resources. What could you do to ensure that your students experience the benefits of learning with technology?

Assessment Ideas

Portfolio Assessment

You can use Activities 5.1, *Ways in Which You Have Used Technologies for Learning*, and 5.2, *Why Should Children Use Learning Technology?*, to assess your students' prior ideas about technology. Most of the remaining activities guide students in exploring a variety of learning technologies. Although each of these examples is a valuable learning experience for your students to complete in class, you may decide to have your students include only one or two of these in their portfolios or that you will use for assessment.

Learning Technology Evaluation

When your students present their evaluation of a learning technology, they demonstrate their ideas about how technology can support student learning. Students should describe the learning benefits provided by the tool, what it does not help with, what might be an issue with the tool, and practical issues.

Technology-Enhanced Lesson Development

Your students should develop a technology-enhanced lesson that addresses science ideas related to their unit's driving question. This lesson should focus on one technology tool selected to support a specific aspect of their project such as investigation or artifact development or a benchmark lesson. Lesson descriptions should include technology-specific components such as (1) pre-technology activities, (2) learning about the technology, (3) technology activities, and (4) post-technology activities. Also, this investigation lesson is not necessarily a one-class-period lesson. Rather, it should be an extended lesson spanning multiple class periods. Finally, students should write a rationale statement describing how the technology tool in their lesson supports students in understanding the science ideas.

Resources

Text Resources

Amati, K. (1999). Constructing scientific models in middle school. In J. Minstrell and E. V. Zee (Eds.), *Inquiry into Inquiry Science Learning and Teaching*. (pp. 316-329). Washington, D.C.: American Association for the Advancement of Science Press.

Berger, C., Lu, C., Belzer, S., and Voss, B. (1996). Research on the uses of technology in science education. In B. J. Fraser and K. G. Tobin (Eds.), *International Handbook of Science Education* (pp. 466–490). Dordrecht, The Netherlands: Kluwer Academic Publishers.

Brasell, H. (1987). The effect of real-time laboratory graphing on learning graphic representations of distance and velocity. *Journal of Research in Science Teaching*, 24(4): 385–395.

Edelson, D. C., Gordin, D. N., and Pea, R. D. (1999). Addressing the challenges of inquiry-based learning through technology and curriculum design. *Journal of the Learning Sciences*, 8(3-4): 391–450.

Krajcik, J. S., Blumenfeld, P. C., Marx, R. W., and Soloway, E. (1999). Instructional, curricular, and technological supports for inquiry in science classrooms. In J. Minstrell and E. V. Zee (Eds.), *Inquiry into Inquiry Science Learning and Teaching*. Washington, D.C.: American Association for the Advancement of Science Press.

Linn, M. (1993). Using technology to teach thermodynamics: Achieving integrated understanding. In D. L. Ferguson (Ed.), *Advanced Educational Technologies for Mathematics and Science* (pp. 5–60). New York: Springer-Verlag.

Novak, A., and Gleason, C. (2001). Incorporating portable technology to enhance inquiry: Project-based middle school science classroom. In R. Tinker and J. Krajcik (Eds.), *Portable Technologies: Science Learning in Context*. Netherlands: Kluwer Publishers.

Songer, N. B. (1998). Can technology bring students closer to science? In B. J. Fraser and K. G. Tobin (Eds.), *International Handbook of Science Education* (Vol. 1, pp. 333–347). Dordrecht, The Netherlands: Kluwer Academic Publishers.

Songer, N. B., Lee, H.-S., and Kam, R. (2002). Technology-rich inquiry science in urban classrooms: What are the barriers to inquiry pedagogy? *Journal of Research in Science Teaching*, 39(2): 128–150.

Spitulnik, M. W., Stratford, S. J., Krajcik, J. S., and Soloway, E. (1998). Using technology to support students' artifact construction in science. In B. J. Fraser and K. G. Tobin (Eds.), *International Handbook of Science Education* (Vol. 1, pp. 363–381). Dordrecht, The Netherlands: Kluwer Academic Publishers.

Tinker, R. (1996). *The Problem of Extended Inquiry in Science Teaching: Technology-Rich Curricula to the Rescue*. http://www.concord.org: Concord Consortium.

Wu, H.-K., Krajcik, J. S., and Soloway, E. (2001). Promoting understanding of chemical representations: Students' use of a visualization tool in the classroom. *Journal of Research in Science Teaching*, 38(7): 821–842.

Internet Resources

You can access all of these sites directly on the Instructor's area of the Online Learning Center. Web addresses will be updated there as changes are made.

American Association of University Women (http://www.aauw.org/2000/techsavvy.html): Information on equity issues in technology.

Artemis (http://webartemis.org): On-line collection specifically designed for middle and high school students. The Web resources within the digital library have been preselected by librarians, keeping in mind the learning needs and reading levels of students.

Concord Consortium (http://www.concord.org): The Concord Consortium is a nonprofit educational research and development organization. They create interactive materials that exploit the power of information technologies.

Eisenhower National Clearing House (http://www.enc.org): ENC identifies effective curriculum resources, create high-quality professional development materials, and disseminates useful information and products to improve K-12 mathematics and science teaching and learning.

FeederWatch (http://birds.cornell.edu/pfw): Project FeederWatch is a winter-long survey of birds that visit feeders at backyards, nature centers, community areas, and other locales in North America. FeederWatch helps scientists track broadscale movements of winter bird populations and long-term trends in bird distribution and abundance.

Genscope (http://genscope.concord.org): Computer-based manipulative (CBM) tool that enables students to investigate scientific and mathematical concepts related to genetics through direct manipulation and experimentation.

GLOBE, Global Learning and Observations to Benefit the Environment (http://www.globe.gov): GLOBE is a worldwide hands-on, primary and secondary school-based science and education program. GLOBE provides students the opportunity to learn by collecting data, mapping, and sharing ideas through the Internet related to atmosphere, hydrology, soils, and land cover/phenology.

Highly Interactive Computing in Education, hi-ce (http://hi-ce.org): Source of technology software tools to support student learning including Model-It, applications for handhelds, and Artemis.

HyperStudio (http://www.hyperstudio.com): Software to support student-created multimedia products.

Imagiworks (http://www.imagiworks.com): The ImagiProbe and ImagiLab family of products transforms handheld computers into sensor-based, portable laboratory systems with a combination of hardware, software and educational content.

International Society for Technology Education, ISTE (http://www.iste.org/resources/index.html): Teacher resources page with listings of current Web sites, books, or periodicals that relate to educational technology including lesson plans.

Kids as Global Scientists (http://www.onesky.umich.edu/kgs01.html): Inquiry-based middle school weather curriculum using the educational potential of current computer technologies in science classes; weather curriculum, hands-on science investigations, real-time information from the Internet, telecommunication through an electronic message board, and an Internet-smart CD-ROM.

Learning Technologies in Urban Schools, LeTUS (http://www.letus.org): Source of educational technology tools to support student learning with real-world data.

MERLOT (http://www.merlot.org/Home.po): MERLOT is a free and open resource designed primarily for faculty and students of higher education. Links to online learning materials are collected here along with annotations such as peer reviews and assignments.

One Sky Many Voices (http://www.onesky.umich.edu/index.html): Science curricula that utilize CD-ROM and the World Wide Web; program centered on environmental science themes run during a set time period to coordinate learning among participants.

PASCO (http://www.pasco.com): Probeware, software, and activity guides for student science investigations.

SciLinks (http://www.scilinks.org/tour): SciLinks is an exciting partnership between progressive U.S. textbook publishers and NSTA, the largest organization of science educators in the world. If your textbook has SciLinks, you and your students will have the best Internet science sources at your fingertips all preselected and preapproved by NSTA's network of teacher–Webwatchers.

Texas Instruments (http://education.ti.com/index.html): Calculator-based labs, probeware, and software.

Tom Snyder Productions (http://www.teachtsp.com): Support for teachers to use technology in the classroom based on their collection of CD-ROM-based materials designed to engage elementary and middle school students in solving today's real-world problems with science.

Vernier (http://www.vernier.com): Probeware, software, and activity guides for student science investigations.

Window to the Universe Project (http://www.windows.ucar.edu): A fun and different Web site about the Earth and space sciences; Windows to the Universe is graphics intensive.

WorldWatcher (http://www.worldwatcher.nwu.edu/software.htm): WorldWatcher, a supportive scientific visualization environment for the investigation of scientific data that provides an accessible and supportive environment for students to explore, create, and analyze scientific data.

CHAPTER 6
HOW DO I DEVELOP COLLABORATION IN THE SCIENCE CLASSROOM?

Chapter Overview

Collaboration is an important component of project-based classrooms. This chapter describes the nature of collaboration and the benefits of creating a collaborative learning environment. Collaboration differs from other group situations when children are simply put into groups without developing collaborative skills. Strategies for teaching children how to work collaboratively in a group include goal sheets, task completion skills, progress reports, icebreaker activities, win–win charts, and division of labor.

Various challenges to creating a collaborative environment are presented, as are suggestions for addressing these challenges. Teachers can actively work with students to prevent problems, including status-differential effect, group pacts, and socially induced incompetence. The reasons collaboration almost always works better than individual learning include creating multiple zones of proximal development, raising achievement and enhancing problem-solving abilities, developing deep understandings, and helping to spread the cognitive load among group members.

Chapter Learning Performances

- Describe various types of collaboration.

- Explain the role a teacher can play in supporting collaboration.

- Clarify challenges that a teacher might need to overcome to implement collaborative learning groups.

- Describe how to help children learn skills needed to work in collaborative groups.

- Critique learning environments to determine their ability to foster collaborative learning.

- Design and implement different types of collaborative learning environments.

- Explain why collaborative learning is almost always better than individual learning and explain how it particularly helps female and minority students pursue science study.

Lesson Ideas

The Nature of Collaboration

Portfolio Activity 6.1 is an introduction to the topic of collaboration. However, if collaboration has been a component of your classroom, your students have already been introduced to the concept.

Portfolio Activity 6.1 *How Does Collaboration Change the Nature of the Classroom?:* Observing a truly collaborative classroom is a great learning experience for your students.

> **Tip:** Collaboration is often confused with cooperation. Many teachers find cooperative learning strategies easier to understand and implement. It takes time to develop collaborative skills both for students and teachers.

Types of Collaborative Learning

If possible, incorporate several types of collaboration in your classroom. This begins with the small-group and whole-class discussions and activities throughout Chapters 1 to 5. In addition, you can set up a class email list. You and your students can use this list to continue class discussions, post and answer questions, and share ideas. You will need to initiate the email conversations. You can post discussion questions related to the reading or class activities. Of course you also will want to post reminders and other course information. This may not be using the email list for collaboration, but it will encourage students to check their email regularly. You might also encourage participation in the email conversation by requiring students to post questions or responses.

Another idea for encouraging collaboration beyond the walls of the classroom is to include other faculty, scientists, and teachers. Ideally, your students have collaborated with fellow students, but also with you and other instructors and their cooperating teachers in their field experience classrooms. Experienced teachers can collaborate with their fellow teachers, administrators, and parents. These collaborative connections are particularly appropriate for supporting students in developing their own project plans.

Creating a Collaborative Environment

Your classroom is the best example of a collaborative learning environment. Your students can benefit from collaboration throughout each chapter. Also, students develop collaborative relationships over time. Therefore, many of the collaborative strategies described here need to be initiated early in your course. For example, in the Project Example and Project Development activities, your students are working in groups. You can refer to strategies for forming groups described in this chapter. Thus, groups for the Project Example can be groups of three or four, because there are many tasks involved in the investigations. However, Project Development groups can be groups of two, to allow more input from each student. If students are working on individual projects, they should still work in groups of two for sharing ideas and giving feedback as they develop plans and lessons.

> Visual Resources: Table 6.1 Factors to Consider When Forming Groups, available in the Instructor's area of the Online Learning Center.

Portfolio Activities 6.2 through 6.8 in this section address individual strategies for supporting student collaboration. You can incorporate these portfolio activities as part of the class's Project Example. One way to this is to replace the specific content of the portfolio activity with that of the class project example. For example, Portfolio Activity 6.6, *How Can You Help Students Build Understanding?*, uses a general investigation selected from a science book. Instead, your students could examine one of the investigations from the Project Example. Alternatively, you could have the class complete each of the portfolio activities as written and add your class's investigation to the activity.

Project Example

All of the strategies described in the text to support student collaboration will also be helpful for your students. You can support your students in collaboration during their inquiry into boat design with these same strategies. Your students will revisit these strategies when they begin to develop their collaboration plans for students as part of their project plans.

> **Tip:** Like children, your students also will need to learn how to collaborate. You may need to scaffold their initial conversations and help them negotiate differences.

Portfolio Activity 6.2 *How Do I Introduce Collaborative Skills to Students?*

Portfolio Activity 6.3 *Making T-Charts:* This is a good activity to do in class.

Portfolio Activity 6.4 *How Do Children Build Trust in a Group?*

> Visual Resources: Boxes in Portfolio Activity 6.4, available in the Instructor's area of the Online Learning Center.

Portfolio Activity 6.5 *What Skills Are Helpful in Cooperative Groups?*

Project Example

If you have not already done so, you should have your students present their findings and conclusions from the investigation described in Chapter 4. The second investigation in the project *How can I predict if a boat will float?* is a good investigation for discussing and critiquing different ideas. Because each group developed its own investigation question and design, each investigation will be different. Students should discuss their evidence for their ideas about what factors influence floating. This class discussion should include a reflection on how collaboration supported their own learning and what would be different with children. This will transition your students to begin planning a collaboration plan for students.

> **Tip:** Your students may be uncomfortable critiquing the work of other students. Challenging someone's data collection methods or conclusions seems unkind to students who have not experienced this type of discussion before. The students who are presenting their ideas may be uneasy or hurt by what they first perceive as harsh criticism. You will need to model appropriate ways to critique or disagree with data present by your students. Be careful to focus on the data and analysis, not on students' abilities. You should also explain to your students what you are doing and then have students take over the role of critic in the discussion.

Portfolio Activity 6.6 *How Can You Help Students Build Understanding?*

Using Technology Tools to Create a Collaborative Environment

The class email list is one example of using technology to create a collaborative environment that your students can discuss. Other examples to explore include Project FeederWatch and Kids as Global Scientists. Your students may be familiar with these examples from activities in Chapter 5, *How Can Learning Technologies Be Used to Support Investigations?* Now they are exploring these tools from the viewpoint of supporting collaboration.

Portfolio Activity 6.7 *How Do Roles Facilitate Collaborative Learning?:* This technology-based activity focuses on collaboration and science ideas and is great to do as a whole-class activity.

Challenges That Arise When Students Collaborate in Small Groups

Portfolio Activity 6.8 *Troubleshooting:* Add scenarios from your students' experiences observing or teaching in the classroom. Group troubleshooting is particularly useful for student teachers who may have difficulty with initial teaching experiences.

Portfolio Activity 6.9 *How Do I Explain Collaborative Learning to Colleagues and Parents?:* Your students should keep these letters as part of their professional teaching portfolio. These letters will be a great resource when they begin teaching in their own classrooms. Your students who are already teaching can use these letters immediately.

Why Collaboration Almost Always Works Better Than Individual Learning

Portfolio Activity 6.10 *How Do Teachers' Roles Change in a Collaborative Classroom?*

Portfolio Activity 6.11 *How Does Collaboration Change the Nature of the Classroom?*

Collaboration Plan Development

Have your students develop a plan for structuring collaborative activities they would use with students. You will need to give your students some guidelines for what they should include in their plans. For example, collaboration plans should include strategies for structuring small-group work and keeping students focused on the science ideas. Encourage your students to use the many tables and strategies described in the text in their own collaboration plans. Have your students share their collaboration plans with the class. A discussion of positive features and suggestions for improvement can help them learn about collaboration strategies and is yet another model of collaboration. Students can then incorporate feedback from you and the class into their revised plans.

Portfolio Activity 6.12 *What Curriculum Resources Use Collaborative Strategies?:* This activity is a good way to have your students evaluate published materials.

Discussion Questions

Remember a time when you were in a science class in college or high school, and you had to work on a group project. What was the task? Did all members of your group work well together? Were there any problems? What were the advantages of working in this group? What were the disadvantages? Compare this situation with the one described in Scenario 4 at the beginning of the textbook chapter. How are these two situations different? How are they alike?

What strengths would a teacher need to have in order to develop a collaborative environment in a science classroom? How do you see yourself in this role? Do you see any challenges for you personally in developing a collaborative classroom?

What are the characteristics of an elementary or middle school collaborative learning classroom? How do these characteristics match the student outcomes advocated in the AAAS Benchmarks and the teaching standards in the National Science Education Standards?

Give an example of a project that could involve parents, other members in the community, and classrooms from other parts of the country. How could a teacher get people involved in answering the question and contributing ideas to solving the problem?

Discuss how the arrangement of desks and other furniture in a classroom can contribute to a collaborative classroom environment or detract from this environment. What issues are important in facilitating students working in groups and the movement of students in the classroom as they carry out different tasks?

What metaphors could you use to describe the teacher's role in a collaborative classroom? Examples might include teacher as facilitator, teacher as model, teacher as guide, and teacher as learner. Give examples for each of these metaphors using your own experiences in science classrooms.

Assessment Ideas

Portfolio Assessment

Portfolio Activities 6.8, *Troubleshooting*, 6.9, *How Do I Explain Collaborative Learning to Colleagues and Parents?*, and 6.12, *What Curriculum Resources Use Collaborative Strategies?*, are particularly useful for assessing students' understanding of collaboration. In each of these tasks students need to apply their ideas about collaboration to support students in collaboration.

Project Example

Have your students write a reflection statement about their experiences with collaboration during each phase of the project *How can I predict if a boat will float?* or the other example project conducted during class. Have your students reflect on these questions.

- What were the best instances of collaboration?

- How did collaboration help you learn?

- How would collaboration be different for children?

- What would improve the collaboration in this project?

Collaboration Plan Development

In a continuation of their project planning students should develop a plan for structuring collaboration in conjunction with activities in one or more lessons of their units. This plan should include some of the suggested strategies described in the text adapted for their specific lessons. Also, this collaboration plan is not necessarily one class period. This plan may be part of an extended lesson spanning multiple class periods. Finally, students should write a rationale statement describing how their plan supports students in talking to each other about ideas.

Resources

Text Resources

American Association for the Advancement of Science (1990). *Science for All Americans*. New York: Oxford University Press.

American Association for the Advancement of Science (1993). *Benchmarks for Science Literacy*. New York: Oxford University Press.

Brown, A. L., and Campione, J. C. (1994). Guided discovery in a community of learners. In K. McGilly (Ed.), *Classroom Lessons: Integrating Cognitive Theory and Classroom Practice* (pp. 229–270). Cambridge, MA: MIT Press/Bradford Books.

Brown, J. S., Collins, A., and Duguid, P. (1989). Situated cognition and the culture of learning. *Educational Researcher*, 18(Jan-Feb): 32–42.

Lave, J., and Wenger, E. (1991). *Situated Learning: Legitimate Peripheral Participation*. New York: Cambridge University Press.

Marshall, Hermine (Ed). (1992). *Redefining Student Learning: Roots of Educational Change*. Norwood, NJ: Ablex.

Rogoff, B. (1994). Developing understanding of the idea of communities of learners. *Mind, Culture, and Activity*, 4: 209–229.

Vygotsky, L. S. (1978). *Mind in Society: The Development of Higher Psychological Processes* (M. Cole, V. John-Steiner, S. Scriber, and E Souberman, Eds. and translators). Cambridge, MA: Harvard University Press.

Internet Resources

You can access all of these sites directly on the Instructor's area of the Online Learning Center. Web addresses will be updated there as changes are made.

Ask-A Geologist (http://walrus.wr.usgs.gov/docs/ask-a-ge.html): Opportunity for students to email questions about volcanoes, earthquakes, mountains, rocks, maps, ground cover, lakes and rivers; different USGS scientists respond in a few days.

Collaborative Software Laboratory (CSL) (http://coweb.cc.gatech.edu/csl): Computer-supported collaborative learning with an emphasis on collaboration; variety of computer applications to support student learning and collaboration.

FeederWatch (http://birds.cornell.edu/pfw): Project FeederWatch is a winter-long survey of birds that visit feeders at backyards, nature centers, community areas, and other locales in North America. FeederWatchers periodically count the highest numbers of each species they see at their feeders from November through early April and send their data to scientist over the Internet.

Kids as Global Scientists (http://www.onesky.umich.edu/kgs01.html): Inquiry-based middle school weather curriculum using real-time information from the Internet, telecommunication through an electronic message board, and an Internet-smart CD-ROM.

SJSU Virtual Museum (www.sjsu.edu/depts/Museum/aamenu.html): The History of Mathematics, Science, and Technology: A Culturally Affirming View; biographies of scientists; opportunity to nominate scientists to be included.

The Biology Project (http://www.biology.arizona.edu): University of Arizona on-line interactive resource for learning biology.

U.S. Fish & Wildlife Service Endangered Species Program (http://endangered.fws.gov): Information about endangered species; programs for students including interactive learning games.

CHAPTER 7
HOW DO I DEVELOP AND USE BENCHMARK LESSONS?

Chapter Overview

This chapter explores the role of benchmark lessons in a project environment and discusses their importance. Benchmark lessons serve several purposes. They help children learn difficult science concepts, illustrate laboratory techniques, build new inquiry abilities, model thinking, and stimulate curiosity. The chapter describes how to use concept maps, listen to students, and use the KWL technique in determining when to use a benchmark lesson. Several models for planning benchmark lessons are presented, including formatted lesson plans, the learning cycle model, and the expanded 5-E model.

Many strategies and techniques that teachers can use in benchmark lessons are described, including demonstrations, large-group discussions, presentations (metaphors, diagrams, graphs, videos; guest lectures), and community resources. Strategies to make benchmark lessons more active include role-playing, teacher-planned activities, investigation centers, and field trips. Teachers can also use literature, including children's books, magazines, and the World Wide Web. Finally, concept maps and questioning are discussed. In project-based science, ideas and principles must be related to a driving question that is meaningful to students, even in benchmark lessons.

Chapter Learning Performances

- Explain why benchmark lessons are a critical component of project-based science.

- Describe how a teacher can determine when to plan a benchmark lesson.

- Create a lesson plan for and teach a benchmark lesson.

- Compare and contrast the reasons for using various types of strategies (demonstrations, large-group discussion, etc.) for benchmark lessons.

- Explain the value of using children's literature in science and suggest literature that can be used to teach a science concept.

- Justify why concept maps are useful and create a concept map for a science concept to be taught.

- Distinguish among various types of questions.

Lesson Ideas

The Role of Benchmark Lessons in Project-based Science

You have probably included several benchmark lessons in your course before this chapter. Depending on the types of activities you have used thus far, your students will be familiar with some the strategies and techniques described here in Chapter 7. For example, concept mapping was first suggested in Chapters 1 and 2. KWL was used as part of the project example in Chapter 3 on driving questions. As described in the text, these activities were suggested to help you and your students identify concepts and skills to address during this course.

Portfolio Activity 7.1 *What Is a Concept?:* This initial brainstorming is a good way to begin a list of concepts or words to include in a concept map.

If you have not already done so, have your students create concept maps of their ideas about a science topic. You can have your students create concept maps illustrating their understanding of the science ideas associated with the project example *How can I predict if a boat will float?* or another project example topic.

Portfolio Activity 7.2 *Building a Concept Map*

> **Tip:** Students tend to omit linking words when creating their first concept maps. Remind your students to describe each link.

Portfolio Activity 7.3 *Developing a Concept Map to Identify Benchmark Lessons:* In contrast to other concept-mapping activities, your students should use these maps to identify benchmark lessons. Have your students include a description of how their maps helped them identify benchmark lessons.

Concept Map

Your students can create a concept map of the concepts in their project they are developing. Using their maps, your students can then identify places for benchmark lessons. This concept map can replace or be added to Portfolio Activity 7.3, *Developing a Concept Map to Identify Benchmark Lessons*.

Planning a Benchmark Lesson

Have your students develop several learning performance statements. They can develop learning performances for topics you supply or for the benchmark lessons they identified using their concept maps. To help them think about appropriate science ideas for student learning, have your students revisit their topic in *National Science Education Standards* (NRC, 1996) and *Benchmarks for Science Literacy* from Project 2061 (AAAS, 1993; 1990). In addition, Project 2061's *Atlas for Science Literacy* (AAAS, 2001) will also be useful to help your students think about prerequisite knowledge or skills.

> Visual Resources: Table 7.5 Learning Performances, available in the Instructor's area of the Online Learning Center.

Using Table 7.5 your students can match each of their learning performances to one of the cognitive dimensions. Alternatively, as a whole class, students can develop a learning performance for each dimension in the table.

> **Tip:** It is not likely that your class will be able to completely fill this table by using only one topic area. Choose topics from any area listed in *Standards* or *Benchmarks*.

> Visual Resources: Figure 7.3 Curriculum Planning Model for Project-Based Science, available in the Instructor's area of the Online Learning Center.

> Visual Resources: Figure 7.4 The 5-E Model, available in the Instructor's area of the Online Learning Center.

To help your students to begin thinking about how to plan a benchmark lesson, have them compare some example lessons to the 5-E model. Ask students to find a lesson described in a recent issue of *Science and Children* or *Science Scope* that engages students in hands-on activity or investigation.

Identify the parts of the learning cycle model or the 5-E model with the parts of this lesson. Are there any missing parts? How could you modify this lesson or enhance it to make it more aligned with the model?

> **Tip:** Your students may be familiar with many of the specific strategies described in this chapter, such as the 5-E model, demonstrations, or searching the Web. In project-based science, however, these activities are always connected to a driving question.

Portfolio Activity 7.4 *Planning and Teaching a Benchmark Lesson:* Have your students use the lesson plan format described in the text or another similar format.

Benchmark Lesson Development

Have your students develop a benchmark lesson as part of their own project planning. Your students should be working in pairs throughout their project development phases, but may be working on individual projects. If so, have them work on only one lesson for one of their two projects.

Have your students begin by developing one or more learning performances for a benchmark lesson identified from their concept maps. They should refer to *Standards* or *Benchmarks* and Table 7.5, Learning Performances. Have your students use the lesson plan format described in the text or another similar format. This lesson should incorporate at least one of the strategies or techniques described in this chapter. Therefore, your students' planning should be an ongoing process throughout this chapter. Finally, students can share this lesson with the class through peer teaching or demonstration/description. Everyone can offer feedback on the lesson by commenting on what was done well and offering ideas for improvement.

Using Demonstrations

Lead the class in one of the portfolio activities or another demonstration. If possible, use a discrepant event related to the class's driving question or one of the topics students are exploring in their plans. In your whole-class demonstration use a strategy such as Predict–Observe–Explain (POE). *Invitations to Science* by Liem is one good source of ideas for interesting demonstrations.

Portfolio Activity 7.5 *Heating Water in a Paper Cup*

Portfolio Activity 7.6 *The Inverted Jar*

Using Large-Group Discussion

You can demonstrate a whole-class discussion of the concept illustrated in your demonstration lesson. Your students also have participated in several class discussions in earlier chapters. You might decide to incorporate examination of verbal comments into one of those discussions. You can do this by videotaping the discussion and viewing the tape during this chapter.

> Visual Resources: Table 7.6, Tracking Teacher's Verbal Comments during Discussions, available in the Instructor's area of the Online Learning Center.

Portfolio Activity 7.7 *Leading a Discussion*

Presenting Information

Give your students time to explore the variety of resources available to teachers to assist in presenting information. Students will need a list of suggested sources and access to the Web, catalogs, and your school's science education library. Many resources are listed at the end of this chapter.

Portfolio Activity 7.8 *Finding Images on the World Wide Web:* This activity can be incorporated into the creation of a multimedia document to illustrate a concept related to the class's driving question. Explain that the sources of images and other Web-based materials must be cited.

Portfolio Activity 7.9 *What Educational Value Do Community Resources Have?:* This is a good activity to help student teachers to become familiar with their school's community.

Using Literature

There are many wonderful children's books and magazines appropriate for science teaching. Have a selection available for your students to check out and read. You might want to make a list for your librarian to put on reserve at your school's science education library.

Portfolio Activity 7.10 *Planning and Teaching Another Benchmark Lesson:* This can be the benchmark lesson students are developing as part of their own project planning described earlier in this chapter.

Portfolio Activity 7.11 *How Can I Use a Children's Science Magazine?:* Use Tables 7.7, Constructing Meaning from Text, and 7.8, Monitoring and Evaluating Text Materials, to guide your students' examination of children's science magazines. You can include children's trade books in this activity.

Using Concept Maps

Use one of the concept maps your students created to focus a discussion on how to help students develop maps. If your students worked on revising one of their earlier maps, they should compare both versions to see how their maps and thinking improved. Have your students reflect on their initial experiences developing maps and what they found to be difficult and beneficial.

> **Tip:** Your students probably demonstrated some of or all of the issues described in the text, including reluctance to include a hierarchy, linking words, or arrows. Concept mapping is a difficult cognitive activity. Remind them that thinking hard is beneficial as well as being hard work.

Using Questions

Visual Resources: Table 7.9 Question Classification Scheme, available in the Instructor's area of the Online Learning Center.

Portfolio Activity 7.12 *Identifying Levels of Questions:* Add questions from examples your students have heard in their college science classes or classroom observations, or have included in their own lesson plans.

Portfolio Activity 7.13 *Analyzing Your Questioning Style:* Have your students reflect on how watching videotape of their lesson helped them think about their teaching.

> **Tip:** Teachers often do not realize they are asking only one type of question. Videotape of classroom or peer teaching can be a powerful way for your students to observe their own questioning style.

Discussion Questions

How are benchmark lessons different from traditional lessons planned for a science unit?

When planning a benchmark lesson, how can a teacher take into account constructivist views of learning? (See Chapter 2 for a description of constructivist views of learning and teaching.)

What would you do if in the middle of teaching a planned benchmark lesson, a student raised her hand and initiated a question related to the lesson, but not what you had planned to discuss? Imagine that your benchmark lesson related to plant growth, and that during the lesson a student asked a question about hydroponics: "How can you grow tomatoes without soil?" What would you do?

How are the learning cycle model and the 5-E model consistent with constructivist views of learning? How are these two models consistent with project-based science?

How can a teacher plan a large-group discussion that meets the needs of and engages all students? What techniques described in this chapter for carrying out a large-group discussion would you feel confident using?

Using higher-level questioning requires students to apply new information, synthesize information, and evaluate information. Discuss when it might be appropriate to include planned lower-level questions during a lesson.

Some students may be accustomed to answering the teacher's question by playing "guess the answer the teacher is fishing for." What strategies can you use to assure students that their ideas count?

Assessment Ideas

Portfolio Assessment

In this chapter your students are beginning to plan and practice specific lessons. You can use activity 7.3, *Developing a Concept Map to Identify Benchmark Lessons*, to assess your students' understanding of when and why to use a benchmark lesson. This also is a good way to make sure your students' project plans are on the right track. Activity 7.11, *How Can I Use a Children's Science Magazine?*, is a good example of planning a small part of a lesson. Activities 7.12, *Identifying Levels of Question*, and 7.13, *Analyzing Your Questioning Style*, target students' ideas about questioning and how questions can support student learning. Your students should be able to recognize different levels and types of questions both in writing and in their own practice.

> **Tip:** Your students, both novice and experienced, will probably need more classroom practice before they are able to skillfully use a variety of question types with students.

Concept Map

Your students' concept maps can be evaluated for their understanding of concept maps as a tool to identify benchmark lessons. First, you can evaluate maps for completeness and complexity. Are there aspects of the topic concept obviously missing from the map? Is the map linear, or is it weblike, showing an integrated understanding? Are the links appropriate? Is there an appropriate hierarchy? Then, read their descriptions of what benchmark lessons they might use to help students learn important concepts or skills and how the map helped them identify these benchmark lessons.

Benchmark Lesson Development

Students' benchmark lessons can evaluated on two levels. First, their written descriptions will demonstrate their ability to plan appropriate lessons. Lessons should have clear and appropriate learning performances linked to national or local standards. The instructional sequence should include an engaging introduction for students, accurate content representation, links to the driving question, and a plan for evaluating student learning matched to the learning performances.

Second, their in-class peer teaching or lesson sharing will demonstrate their ability to put their plans into action. Keep in mind that it is normal for students to have more difficulty teaching a lesson than they do writing or planning a lesson. This is an opportunity for your students to practice and receive feedback on their new skills.

Resources

Text Resources

American Association for the Advancement of Science (1990). *Science for All Americans*. New York: Oxford University Press.

American Association for the Advancement of Science (1993). *Benchmarks for Science Literacy*. New York: Oxford University Press.

American Association for the Advancement of Science. (2001). *Atlas of Science Literacy*. Washington, D.C.: American Association for the Advancement of Science and National Science Teachers Association Press.

Liem, T. (1990). *Invitations to Science* (2nd ed.). Science Inquiry Enterprise.

National Research Council. (1996). *National Science Education Standards*. Washington, D.C.: National Academy Press.

Project WET (1995). *Project WET Curriculum and Activity Guide*. Houston TX: The Watercourse and Council for Environmental Education.

Project Wild (1992). *Project Wild Activity Guide*. Bethesda, MD: Western Regional Environmental Education Council.

Project Wild (1992). *Aquatic Project Wild Aquatic Education Activity Guide*. Bethesda, MD: Western Regional Environmental Education Council.

Internet Resources

You can access all of these sites directly on the Instructor's area of the Online Learning Center. Web addresses will be updated there as changes are made.

Animal Pictures Archive (http://www.animalpicturesarchive.com): Indexed archive of animal photos, art, animated graphics, etc.

Arbor Scientific (http://arborsci.com/index2.htm): Suppliers of scientific equipment for schools.

Artemis (http://webartemis.org): On-line collection specifically designed for middle and high school students. The Web resources within the digital library have been preselected by librarians, keeping in mind the learning needs and reading levels of students.

AskERIC Lesson Plans (http://ericir.syr.edu/Virtual/Lessons): The "Ask ERIC Lesson Plan Collection" contains more than 1,000 unique lesson plans which have been written and submitted to Ask ERIC by teachers from all over the United States.

CELLS Alive! (http://www.cellsalive.com): Contains film and computer-enhanced images of living cells and organisms for education and medical research. Library contains live recordings and computer animations of various cells and cell structures that can be used in the classroom.

Classification of Living Things (http://anthro.palomar.edu/animal/default.htm): Tutorial that teaches about the Linnaean system of classification. Correct pronunciations of difficult words can be heard with audio clips. Focuses on how humans fit into the classification system.

Earth911 (http://www.earth911.org): Every day is Earth Day; it is the mission of Earth911 to empower the public with community-specific resources to improve their quality of life.

eNature.com (http://enature.com): Information about wildlife including backyard, bird watching, endangered species, and more; "ask the expert" question posting.

Great Lakes Information Network (http://www.great-lakes.net): The Great Lakes Information Network (GLIN) is a partnership that provides one place on-line for people to find information relating to the binational Great Lakes–St. Lawrence region of North America. GLIN offers a wealth of data and information about the region's environment, economy, tourism, education, and more.

International Carnivorous Plant Society (http://www.carnivorousplants.org): Everything you ever wanted to know about carnivorous plants.

PicoMap (http://www.handheld.hice-dev.org/download.htm): Concept mapping software for handhelds.

Soil Science Society of America (http://www.soils.org): The purpose of this Web site is to advance the discipline and practice of soil science by acquiring and distributing information about soils in relation to crop production, environmental quality, ecosystem sustainability, bioremediation, waste management and recycling, and wise land use.

The Concept Mapping Homepage (http://users.edte.utwente.nl/lanzing/cm_home.htm): A concept mapping homepage that provides an example of a concept map and literature supporting use of concept maps; links to other resources.

The Nine Planets (http://www.ex.ac.uk/Mirrors/nineplanets): Multimedia tour of the solar system; overview of the history, mythology, and current scientific knowledge of each of the planets and moons in our solar system; example of background information for benchmark lessons on space science.

Volcano World (http://volcano.und.nodak.edu): University of North Dakota, information on volcanoes for students, teachers, and the public.

Chapter Overview

This is the first of two chapters that focus on assessment. This chapter explores the purpose and nature of assessment and the advantages and disadvantages of large-scale assessments. High-quality assessments are responsive to context, embedded in instruction, and multidimensional. Current assessments also engage students in the assessment process, are valid and reliable, match today's educational goals, accommodate cultural diversity, are consistent with learning theory, and measure meaningful understanding. Assessment should focus on measurement of learning performances across a variety of knowledge domains. Both formative and summative assessments are discussed. Finally, technology tools can help teachers network with other teachers to examine their assessment practices.

Chapter Learning Performances

- Explain why assessment is a critical component of project-based science.

- Distinguish between classroom assessment and large-scale assessment.

- Explain the value of using various assessment techniques to promote learning for populations of students traditionally at risk in science learning.

- Compare traditional assessment techniques to current assessment techniques.

- Create learning performances and corresponding assessments for content, procedural, and metacognitive knowledge across different cognitive dimensions.

- Justify why a variety of different assessment approaches should be used during different time frames in science classrooms.

- Identify ways in which teachers can network with colleagues to improve their assessment practices.

Lesson Ideas

The Purpose of Assessment

As with other topics in this text, your students will have many experiences with and ideas about assessment. These experiences and ideas will influence their teaching and assessment practices. Portfolio Activities 8.1 and 8.2 are good activities for beginning a discussion about your students' experiences with assessment and their ideas about why teachers should assess children in science.

Portfolio Activity 8.1 *What Is the Purpose of Assessment?*

Portfolio Activity 8.2 *How Do Teachers' Beliefs about Instruction Affect Their Methods of Assessment?*

Have your students share their experiences and ideas about assessment in small groups or whole-class discussion. Listen for ideas or experiences that you will need to address during this chapter.

Tip: Many teachers equate assessment with testing and grading. Throughout this and the next chapter, emphasize the role of assessment in knowing what students know.

Portfolio Activity 8.3 *High-Stakes Testing:* Bring in a sample of public release items from the National Assessment of Educational Progress (NAEP), from the Third International Mathematics and Science Study (TIMMS), and from your local statewide test in science. If possible, include a performance item from the NAEP test. Have your students read and answer some of the items. What type of knowledge do these items assess? Have students compare their ideas to what the test developers claim the items measure. Do you agree?

Show your class some of the summary data supplied by each assessment organization. Use these reports in a discussion of large-scale assessment. Discuss issues of validity, reliability, and scoring practicality. Discuss the difference between norm-referenced and criterion-referenced tests. What are the values of these assessments? What does the data mean? After reading the items, what does this data tell you about student understanding in science? Do you think there are issues with the assessment?

Tip: Depending on their background, some teachers will not understand the purpose of some large-scale assessments. They may believe all tests measure individual student performance. This is not the case for the NAEP or the TIMMS. These tests are designed to compare groups of students over many years or countries.

The Nature of Classroom Assessment

Portfolio Activity 8.4 *How Does Science Reform Affect Assessment Practices?*

Assessment Criteria Development

Have your students develop a list of criteria for good assessments. Begin with each student noting a few ideas down on paper. Then have students, working in groups of three or four, make as complete a list as possible. They should refer to the text or other resources on assessment. Have groups share their lists with the class. As they share ideas, your students may think of additional ideas or eliminate some based on the class's feedback. The next step is to group items that are similar. Here students may notice some ideas are really the same and can be combined into one item. Again share with the class. At some point you will need to help the class create a final list of criteria that everyone agrees will make a good tool to assess assessments.

Finally, have each student write a reflection statement describing her or his ideas about assessments. Here are some questions to guide students' writing. What does the student feel is the most important criterion for assessment? Why? Explain. How could a teacher use this list of assessment criteria? What types of assessments might match these criteria? Why?

Portfolio Activity 8.5 *What Are the Pitfalls of Traditional Testing?:* This is a good follow-up activity to the assessment criteria development. Here students examine commercial tests that accompany traditional elementary or middle grade textbooks.

What to Assess

Portfolio Activity 8.6 *How Can I Choose a Good Assessment Technique to Measure Understanding?:* This will help students begin thinking about how to develop their own assessment plans.

Assessment Evaluation

Now have each group use the final class assessment criteria to evaluate some assessments. They can begin with some of the sample public release items from the NAEP, TIMMS, or the local statewide science test. They should also look at some other assessments such as performance or artifact assessments. You can find examples in *Science and Children* or *Science Scope*. Do any of these assessments meet all or some of the class's criteria? Why or why not?

> **Tip:** Many students will be disappointed that professionally prepared assessments do not match all of their criteria. Lead a discussion of how each type of assessment has its own value and drawbacks.

Finally, have each student write a reflection statement describing their ideas about assessments. Here are some questions to guide their writing. What types of assessments seemed to score highest in your evaluation? Why? What seemed to be the most difficult criteria for an assessment to meet? Why? What should you do to ensure quality assessments in your classroom?

When to Assess

Visual Resources: Table 8.1 Assessing Learning Performances, available in the Instructor's area of the Online Learning Center.

Visual Resources: Blank version of Table 8.1 Assessing Learning Performances, available in the Instructor's area of the Online Learning Center.

Portfolio Activity 8.7 *Assessing Learning Performances:* Have your students use the blank version of Table 8.1, Assessing Learning Performances, to complete this activity in small groups. Groups then can share their ideas with the class. This activity will prepare students for selecting assessments for their own project topics.

Alternatively, you can have each group focus on the driving questions they are developing for their own projects. Have students think about how to assess understanding in each of the knowledge domains listed in Table 8.1. This can be the first step in preparing an assessment plan in the next chapter.

Using Technology Tools to Examine Assessment

Your students can visit the *NSTA Community* section of the National Science Teachers Association Web site. There they can go to the NSTA discussion board and join the conversation with teachers around the country. This section has forums for specific grade levels, general announcements, job openings, and more.

Discussion Questions

What is the role of assessment in science education today? How might this be problematic? What are possible solutions? How should a beginning teacher approach assessment issues?

What should be the role of assessment in science education? Why? What should teachers do with the information provided by assessments?

What is the value of a good assessment? What are the drawbacks of a poor assessment? Why is creating a good assessment so difficult?

To what extent should teachers and communities rely on large-scale testing? What is its value? Can you think of any benefits or drawbacks to requiring all students to be tested? Why?

Should teachers continue to use assessments provided by commercial textbook publishers? Why or why not?

If performance or alternative assessments are consistent with reform in science education, why are traditional tests so widely used? Why are traditional testing techniques used in large-scale testing? How much weight should be place on these types of test for student promotion? For teacher evaluation? Why?

Assessment Ideas

Portfolio Assessment

You can use Activities 8.4, *How Does Science Reform Affect Assessment Practices?*, and 8.5, *What Are the Pitfalls of Traditional Testing?*, to assess your students' understanding of the value and the role of assessment in project-based science. Activities 8.6, *How Can I Choose a Good Assessment Technique to Measure Understanding?*, and 8.7, *Assessing Learning Performances*, are both good activities to prepare your students to develop their own assessment plans. You can assess these portfolio entries to make sure each student is on the right track and ready to begin his or her own plan.

Assessment Criteria Development

You can observe groups and individuals as they are developing their lists of assessment criteria. This will give you an indication of what ideas your students find challenging. If some students believe assessment is simple, you can point out specific issues they might be overlooking. You also can help students who are struggling to come up with ideas.

Students' individual reflection statements will give students an opportunity to express their ideas about assessment criteria. Students can use the class assessment criteria to describe where they agree and where they do not agree. This will illustrate their ideas about the value of assessment and what makes a good assessment.

Assessment Evaluation

Students' individual reflection statements will illustrate their ideas about the value of different assessment techniques. Your students should recognize that multiple assessments are needed to match all of the important criteria of a good assessment program. This is the first step in developing their own assessment plans in the next chapter.

Resources

Text Resources

Anderson, L. W., and Krathwohl, D. R. (2000). *A Taxonomy for Learning, Teaching, and Assessing: A Revision of Bloom's Taxonomy of Educational Objectives* (abridged ed.). Longman.

Black, P. (1998). Assessment by teachers and the improvement of students' learning. In B. J. Fraser and K. B. Tobin (Eds.), *International Handbook of Science Education* (Vol. 2, pp. 811–822). Dordrecht, The Netherlands: Kluwer Academic Publishers.

Lomask, M. S., Baron, J. B., and Greig, J. (1998). Large-scale science performance assessment in Connecticut: Challenges and resolutions. In B. J. Fraser and K. G. Tobin (Eds.), *International Handbook of Science Education* (Vol. 2, pp. 823–844). Dordrecht, The Netherlands: Kluwer Academic Publishers.

National Research Council (2001). *Knowing What Students Know: The Science and Design of Educational Assessment.* Washington, D.C.: National Academy Press.

Schneider, R. M., Krajcik, J., Marx, R. W., and Soloway, E. (2002). Performance of students in project-based science classrooms on a national measure of science achievement. *Journal of Research in Science Teaching*, 39(5): 410–422.

Stratford, S. J., Krajcik, J. S., and Soloway, E. (1998). Secondary students' dynamic modeling processes: Analyzing reasoning about, synthesizing, and testing models of stream ecosystems. *Journal of Science Education and Technology*, 7(3): 215–234.

Tamir, P. (1998). Assessment and evaluation in science education: Opportunities to learn and outcomes. In B. J. Fraser and K. G. Tobin (Eds.), *International Handbook of Science Education* (Vol. 2, pp. 761–789). Dordrecht, The Netherlands: Kluwer Academic Publishers.

Internet Resources

You can access all of these sites directly on the Instructor's area of the Online Learning Center. Web addresses will be updated there as changes are made.

Benchmarks for Science Literacy (http://www.project2061.org/tools/benchol/bolframe.htm): Entire on-line text of the Benchmarks for Science Literacy from Project 2061 of the American Association for the Advancement of Science.

National Academy of Sciences (http://www.nas.edu): Includes links to entire on-line text of the *National Science Education Standards*. Browse contents and abstracts of *Proceedings of the National Academy of Sciences* with opportunity to access thousands of scientific reports; links to description of books and resources for educators and scientists working together.

National Center for Educational Statistics (http://nces.ed.gov): NCES is the primary federal entity for collecting and analyzing data that are related to education in the United States and other nations.

National Science Education Standards (http://www.nap.edu/books/0309053269/html): Entire on-line text of the National Science Education Standards from the National Research Council.

PALS: Performance Assessment Links in Science (http://www.pals.sri.com): PALS is an on-line, standards-based, continually updated resource bank of science performance assessment tasks indexed via the National Science Education Standards (NSES).

Project 2061 (http://www.project2061.org): Describes *Project 2061* background and goals and the guiding document, *Science for All Americans*; links to on-line text of *Benchmarks for Science Literacy*; links to on-line text of *Blueprints*; description of *Resources for Science Literacy*; highlights the important role of teachers in current science reform.

The Third International Mathematics and Science Study TIMMS (http://nces.ed.gov/TIMSS): Data on the mathematics and science achievement of our students compared to that of students in other countries.

CHAPTER 9
HOW IS STUDENT UNDERSTANDING ASSESSED?

Chapter Overview

This second chapter on assessment highlights the purpose of assessment while exploring a three-phase method of assessing student understanding: gathering information, assembling and presenting assessment information, and evaluating assessment information. Numerous techniques for gathering information include administering tests and quizzes; making observations; keeping anecdotal records; using checklists, interviews, and concept maps; and conducting performance-based assessment. Techniques for improving observations and discussions are discussed and types of tests and testing methods are examined. A number of methods for assembling and presenting information are described, including student writing samples, daily journals, physical products, drawings, music, videotapes, and multimedia documents. The use of portfolios and artifacts to present information is explored, including different methods to document work in portfolios—artifacts, reproductions, attestations, and productions. Four techniques are introduced that teachers can use to evaluate assessment information: scoring rubrics, portfolios, self-assessment, and peer assessment. Holistic and analytic scoring rubrics are compared and procedures for creating rubrics are described. The use of assessment information to give grades and make decisions is examined. How technology tools can enhance the assessment process is explored. Finally, the benefits of assessment for teachers, students, and parents are summarized.

Chapter Learning Performances

- Explain the steps a teacher can use to assess student growth and achievement.

- Create assessments using different strategies to measure content, procedural, and metacognitive knowledge.

- Compare and contrast the reasons for using various types of assessment.

- Describe how a teacher can determine if a test or quiz is well constructed.

- Justify why artifacts and portfolios should be consistent with goals in a project-based environment.

- Design a scoring rubric to evaluate a performance.

- Explain the value of assessment for teachers, students, and parents.

Lesson Ideas

Assessment of Student Understanding

Now is a good time to have your students complete their example projects used throughout your course. When students complete their project examples and develop artifacts to explain the science related to their projects, they will have first-hand experience with this form of assessment. They can then use their artifacts during discussions of assessment techniques in this chapter.

Project Example

If your class is following the example *How can I predict if a boat will float?*, your students should be ready to design and build their boats. Connect back to the driving question and the story read at the beginning of the project (Chapter 3). This story describes the need for a way to ensure boats and ships are not overloaded and in danger of sinking. A Plimsoll line is marked on the side of a boat to indicate a safe water level.

You will want to structure this task in such a way that your students will be challenged to use their understanding of the relevant science ideas. One way to do this is to have them design and build the boat without testing it in the water. In addition, they will need to predict how many passengers (marbles) their boat will safely hold. Students should use what they have learned about the variables related to floating through their investigations. For example, one variable is weight. Your students can measure and adjust the weight of the boat.

> **Tip:** Your students will enjoy this challenge and will be creative in their designs. Boats range from pleasure cruise ships with swimming pools and umbrellas, to arctic explorer boats with scientific equipment, to pirate ships with treasure.

Although they should build boats that do float, that is not the most important part of this artifact. Your students' ideas about forces, equilibrium, and displacement will be demonstrated in their written design rationale. Below are directions to guide your students in building their boats and describing their design.

> **Tip:** Some students will write detailed descriptions with diagrams and annotated calculations. Others will need encouragement to be as complete as possible. Remind them the testing team will evaluate not only their boat but their explanation as well.

Directions for boat designing: Design and build your own boat. Be creative in your design and choice of materials. But make sure it will float! Build your boat based on ideas about why objects float. Your boat should float at your Plimsoll line when the all the passengers are on board. As the designer it is your job to specify the number of passengers your boat is intended to hold and the type of water (Arctic Ocean, Great Lakes, etc.) your boat is intended to sail. Your boat must meet the following guidelines:

- Your boat must be built out of household or recycled materials.

- Your boat must fit inside of the tub of water without touching the sides or bottom.

- It should be neat and sturdy—your boat cannot come apart in the water!

- Your boat should have a Plimsoll mark with designated water conditions and recommended passenger or cargo load.

Design statement: Explain how you designed your boat to ensure that it would float. Use ideas about forces downward and upward on your boat and factors that influence these forces in your explanation.

The next step is to test the boats in water with their passengers. Each group should give their boat to another group for testing.

Directions for boat testing: Test another group's boat. Does it float? Does it float in the recommended water conditions? Did it reach the Plimsoll line with its designated load? Write a report to the boat owners describing their boat's performance and an evaluation of their design statement. Help the owners understand where their ideas were accurate and explain areas where they need help understanding the relevant science ideas. Use ideas about forces downward and upward on the boat and factors that influence these forces in your explanation.

When the boat owners receive their reports from the testing group, give them time to read over the report and ask questions or give explanations. Then have a final class discussion. Revisit ideas and questions listed at the beginning and throughout the project. What have we learned? How have our ideas changed? What would we investigate next if we were to continue this project?

> **Tip:** Everyone's boat probably floated until the passengers were loaded. Then some of them probably tipped over. Center of gravity was not considered. This could be the topic of the next investigation if this project were continued.

The final step of this project is for each student to describe their own understanding of the science ideas to explain floating. They can write responses to these questions:

- What is happening when an object is floating? Describe and explain.

- What is happening when an object sinks? Describe and explain.

- How can you predict if an object will float or sink?

Each group should save their boat design statements and testing reports to include in their portfolio. Each student will have an individual final explanation they should include in their portfolio. Each of these artifacts can be used in the discussion of assessment in this chapter.

Portfolio Activities 9.1 through 9.6 in this section address different types and components of assessments. You can incorporate these portfolio activities as part of the class's project example. One way to this is to replace the specific content of the portfolio activity with that of the class project example. For example, Portfolio Activity 9.3, *Writing a Classroom Test*, does not specify a content or process topic. Your students could write a test for the project example or for the topic of their own project they are developing. Alternatively, you could have the class complete each of the portfolio activities as written and add your class's assessments to the activity. For example, Portfolio Activity 9.2, *Developing a Performance-Based Assessment*, examines two ideas appropriate for elementary or middle grade students. Your class can add science ideas from the project example or their own projects to the task of developing a performance-based assessment.

Portfolio Activity 9.1 *Developing a Skills Checklist:* Your students can develop a skills checklist for one of the activities included in the project example.

> Visual Resources: Table 9.1 Project-Specific Checklist, available in the Instructor's area of the Online Learning Center.

> Visual Resources: Table 9.2 Generic Checklist, available in the Instructor's area of the Online Learning Center.

Portfolio Activity 9.2 *Assessing Affective Attributes:* This activity is an excellent topic for a class discussion. In the discussion you can bring up the assessment of dispositions recommended by the Interstate New Teacher Assessment and Support Consortium (INTASC) for teacher education programs.

Table 9.3 Affective Attributes of Students in Project-Based Science, available in the Instructor's area of the Online Learning Center.

Use one of the concept maps your students created to focus a discussion on how to evaluate concept maps. If your students worked on revising one of their earlier maps, they should compare both versions to see how their maps and thinking improved. Then they can explore how to score concept maps as described in the text.

Visual Resources: Figure 9.1 Limited Concept Map, available in the Instructor's area of the Online Learning Center.

Visual Resources: Figure 9.2 Complex Concept Map, available in the Instructor's area of the Online Learning Center.

Portfolio Activity 9.3 *Writing a Classroom Test:* This test can be for the project example or for the projects the students are developing.

> **Tip:** Novice teachers often have difficulty writing clear directions with enough detail that students can understand what they are being asked to do.

Portfolio Activity 9.4 *Developing a Performance-based Assessment:* Your class can add science ideas from the project example or their own projects to this activity.

> **Tip:** Even teachers who understand that assessments need to match learning performances and instruction may have difficulty writing assessments or rubrics that are actually matched. For example, a teacher might write a performance-based assessment requiring students to name the 10 parts of a microscope rather than assessing students on their ability to use a microscope to view pond water.

Visual Resources: Figure 9.3 Parent Letter, available in the Instructor's area of the Online Learning Center.

Portfolio Activity 9.5 *Creating Your Own Portfolio:* This teaching portfolio is not the same as the portfolio of activities completed in this course, although your students will be able to include many of the same items in each. For example, Activity 9.4, *Developing a Performance-Based Assessment*, can be an example of one type of assessment they will use in their classrooms.

Visual Resources: Table 9.4 Analytic Scoring Rubric, available in the Instructor's area of the Online Learning Center.

Portfolio Activity 9.6 *Developing a Scoring Rubric*

Rubric Development

Your students should use the steps listed in Activity 9.6 to develop a rubric for the project example and then for the project they are developing. In the project example your students can create a rubric for evaluating the boat design statements, the testing reports, or the final explanations. They might also create a rubric for the multimedia document created in Chapter 5 on technology or one of the investigations in Chapter 4 on investigation. You can instruct everyone to create a rubric for the same assessment, or let them choose. Alternatively, you can have your students create a rubric for an assessment in the project they are developing.

Tip: Teachers tend to include many criteria for neat, organized, on time, participates, etc., in their initial rubrics. Emphasize that rubrics should also include criteria for understanding specific concepts and process skills.

Visual Resources: Figure 9.4 The Assessment Process, available in the Instructor's area of the Online Learning Center.

Portfolio Activity 9.7 *Creating a Report Card:* This is a good activity to do in class with small groups.

Another Look at the Advantages of Educational Assessment

Portfolio Activity 9.8 *Efficiency of Assessment*

Have your students read over their initial ideas about assessment written at the beginning of the first chapter on assessment (Chapter 8). Have any ideas changed? If so, how are they different? Are any ideas still the same? How will the students' ideas impact what they will do in the classroom?

Portfolio Activity 9.9 *What Have You Learned About Assessment?:* Your students revisit their ideas listed in Portfolio Activity 8.1, *What is the Purpose of Assessment?*

Assessment Plan Development

Have your students develop a plan for assessment they would use with students. You will need to give your students some guidelines for what they should include in their plans. For example, you could have your students organize their plans by the three phases of assessing student understanding: gathering information, assembling and presenting assessment information, and evaluating assessment information. Also, assessment plans should include multiple opportunities for students to demonstrate understanding, including performance-based assessments. Different types and levels of knowledge should be assessed as described in Table 8.1, Assessing Learning Performances, from Chapter 8. Encourage your students to use the many tables and strategies described in the text in their own assessment plans. Have your students share their assessment plans with the class. A discussion of positive features and suggestions for improvement can help them learn about assessment strategies. Students can then incorporate feedback from you and the class into their revised plans.

Discussion Questions

Compare the use of a variety of assessment types with the current theories of how children learn and the ultimate goal of project-based science. (Note: Key features of the social constructivist model of teaching are described in Chapter 2 and include active engagement with phenomena, using and applying knowledge, multiple representations, use of learning communities, and the role of authentic tasks. The ultimate goal of project-based science is students' integrated understandings.)

Discuss the challenges involved in using the types of assessments discussed in this chapter in place of traditional pencil-and-paper tests. Here are some concerns raised by teachers: How will you store all your students' portfolios? How can you deal with a mountain of papers? What about project displays? What concerns might an administrator or a parent have if you used only authentic assessments instead of traditional quizzes and tests? How would you address these concerns? If you chose to interview your students, how would you have time to interview them?

How can you avoid bias and subjectivity when you use various assessment techniques? Give an example of a specific assessment and defend the validity and reliability of the assessment.

Discuss some of your own experiences in college classes in which teachers used alternative assessments. Did you think the assessment was fair? What were other reactions—your own and those of other students? How do you think these assessments could have been improved? How were these assessments more appropriate than traditional paper-and-pencil tests consisting of mainly multiple-choice and short-answer questions?

How do the variety of techniques for authentic assessments presented in this chapter compare with your own ideas about teaching and learning? Do you have any concerns about using any of these kinds of assessments?

Assessment Ideas

There are multiple opportunities to assess your students' understanding of assessment—more than you need in order to judge their knowledge and skills. Many of the ideas suggested here are variations on the same theme. For example, your students will develop a performance-based assessment in their portfolios. But this can also be the assessment example you chose to evaluate. In addition, they can develop a rubric for scoring this assessment and then include both portions in their assessment plan.

Portfolio Assessment

The activities in this chapter are all valuable components of an assessment plan that your students should keep in their professional teaching portfolios to use in the future. Although your students should do each activity, you do not need to evaluate all of them. You can tell your class which activities you will assess, or you can let them select one for you to assess. Activities 9.1, *Developing a Skills Checklist*, 9.2, *Assessing Affective Attributes*, 9.3, *Writing a Classroom Test,* and 9.4, *Developing a Performance-Based Assessment*, are particularly useful for this assessment.

Assessment Example

Your students' artifacts from their project examples can be assessed for science understanding. This will make the task a real example of artifact assessment and will motivate your students to participate fully. If you are completing the project described in this manual, your students will have a boat design statement, a testing report, and a final explanation of floating. Each of these can be assessed for understanding of forces, equilibrium, and related concepts.

Assessment Development

This can be one of the assessments developed during this chapter as part of the portfolio activities. Depending on which assessment you choose to use as an assessment, you will have slightly different criteria. However, in each case the assessment should align with stated learning performances, match instruction, be valid and reliable, and have clear directions for students. You can let each student choose what assessment they would like you to assess.

Rubric Development

This is one time where you could assess the process of developing the rubric rather than the actual rubric. Your students will work very hard and will need to revise their rubrics more than once. Their final rubric may still need improvement. This type of development is an ongoing process. However, students will demonstrate their understanding of rubrics as evaluation tools through discussions and negotiations over what should be included and how to categorize excellent, satisfactory, or poor.

Assessment Plan Development

In a continuation of their project planning, students should develop a plan for assessment in conjunction with activities in one or more lessons of their unit. This plan should include some of the suggested strategies described in the text, adapted for their specific assessment. Also, this assessment plan is not necessarily one class period. This plan may be part of an extended lesson spanning multiple class periods. It is up to you to decide the scope and completeness of students' plans. You might want only preliminary plans at this point with more complete plans in their final project plans (Chapter 11). Finally, students can write a rationale statement describing how their plans match criteria for good assessments developed by the class in Chapter 8.

> **Tip:** It will be very difficult for your students to develop assessment plans that match all of the criteria developed by the class. However, your student should be able to describe where his or her plan is successful, and where and why it falls short.

Resources

Text Resources

American Association for the Advancement of Science. (1990). *Science for All Americans*. New York: Oxford University Press.

American Association for the Advancement of Science (1993). *Benchmarks for Science Literacy*. New York: Oxford University Press.

Anderson, L. W., and Krathwohl, D. R. (2000). *A Taxonomy for Learning, Teaching, and Assessing: A Revision of Bloom's Taxonomy of Educational Objectives* (abridged ed.). Longman.

Doran, R., Chan, F., and Tamir, P. (1998). *Science Educator's Guide to Assessment*. Arlington, VA: NSTA Press.

Hein, G. E., and Price, S. (1994). *Active Assessment for Active Science: A Guide for Elementary School Teachers*. Portsmouth, NH: Heinemann.

Herman, J., Aschbacher, P., and Winters, L. (1992). *A Practical Guide to Alternative Assessment*. Alexandria, VA: Association for Supervision and Curriculum Development.

Hogan, K. (1994). *Eco-inquiry*. Dubuque, IA: Kendall/Hunt Publishing Company.

National Research Council (1996). *National Science Education Standards*. Washington, D.C.: National Academy Press.

National Research Council (2001). *Knowing What Students Know: The Science and Design of Educational Assessment*. Washington, D.C.: National Academy Press.

White, R., and Gunstone, R. (1992). *Probing Understanding*. London: Farmer Press.

Internet Resources

You can access all of these sites directly on the Instructor's area of the Online Learning Center. Web addresses will be updated there as changes are made.

Information on Rubrics (http://www.csuchico.edu/educ/cguenter/rubrics.html): California State University; links many resources on rubrics.

Practical Assessment Research and Evaluation (http://ericae.net/pare/getvn.asp?v=7&n=3): Scoring rubrics: when and how; information about rubrics.

Project-Based Learning (http://4teachers.org/projectbased/checklist.shtml): Project-Based Learning; checklists for project-based work.

RubiStar (http://rubistar.4teachers.org): RubiStar is a tool to help the teacher who wants to use rubrics but does not have the time to develop them from scratch, to create rubrics for project-based activities.

Tammy's Technology Tips for Teachers (http://www.essdack.org/tips/index.html): Includes ideas for scoring rubrics and use of electronic portfolios.

Technology Support for Alternative Assessment (http://transition.alaska.edu/www/Portfolios/TechPort1.html): Describes important points in using portfolios as alternative assessments.

The Staff Room (http://www.odyssey.on.ca/%7Eelaine.coxon/rubrics.htm): Rubrics from the staff room for Ontario teachers; sample rubrics and tips.

CHAPTER 10
HOW DO I MANAGE THE PROJECT-BASED SCIENCE CLASSROOM?

Chapter Overview

This chapter introduces three key components of the basic management of a project-based science classroom: classroom climate, organization, and management strategies. The classroom climate section describes how a constructivist framework is used to establish a positive classroom environment. In this framework, students participate fully in helping solve classroom problems and forming norms or ground rules. The teacher serves as a role model who promotes a positive attitude toward science and a positive classroom climate. The teacher develops affective factors such as curiosity about the world, excitement about science, and enthusiasm to continue activities and generates strong curriculum that is of interest to students. To develop a positive classroom climate in which students help solve problems, there must be a balanced relationship between the teacher and the students. Finally, in a positive classroom climate all students—boys and girls, minorities and nonminorities—feel capable of learning science.

In the section on classroom organization, aspects of physical facilities, the structure of the school day, and safety are discussed. Specific strategies for managing a project environment are described.

In the section on management strategies, considerations for before, during, and after instruction are described. Considerations before instruction include establishing rules, using contracts, and anticipating problems. Considerations during instruction include distributing materials, making transitions, dealing with disturbances, and working with multiple instances of activities. Finally, after-instruction considerations include reinforcing classroom norms, revisiting and reflecting upon norms, and evaluating progress.

Chapter Learning Performances

- Explain how the constructivist framework is useful for thinking about classroom management in project-based science.

- Describe how a teacher can create an effective classroom climate.

- Create a positive classroom atmosphere.

- Compare and contrast the reasons for using various types of classroom management strategies.

- Explain the value of planning classroom management before, during, and after instruction.

- Justify why equitable classroom practices are necessary for managing project-based science.

- Distinguish among various types of safety precautions.

Lesson Ideas

Classroom Climate

Portfolio Activities 10.1, 10.2, and 10.3 are a good introduction to managing a project-based science classroom. Activity 10.1 introduces the three key components and lists several questions to guide a comparison of the four classroom scenarios at the beginning of the chapter. Activity 10.2 gives your students the opportunity to reflect on their previous experiences with negative and positive classroom climates. Finally, Activity 10.3 begins the discussion of how to actively promote positive classroom climate. Each activity can be part of small-group and whole-class discussion of what it means to use a constructivist framework to create a positive classroom climate.

Portfolio Activity 10.1 *Managing a Science Classroom:* This activity is a good introduction to the three key components of managing a project-based science classroom. In small groups students discuss and evaluate each classroom description. Then groups report and explain their evaluation in a whole-class discussion. This discussion includes suggestions for revising the lessons based on the evaluation.

Portfolio Activity 10.2 *What Makes a Positive Project-Based Science Classroom Climate?*

> **Tip:** Some teachers believe they are expected to maintain tight control over students and worry that their principal or other teachers will disapprove if they do not. In addition, they may misunderstand a constructivist classroom to mean that students are given complete freedom which will lead to chaos. It is important for you to help your students understand the balanced relationship between the students and the teacher which creates a positive classroom climate.

Portfolio Activity 10.3 *Promoting Positive Affective Factors:* The ideas discussed in this activity will help your students develop their own management plan later in this chapter.

> Visual Resources: Table 10.1 Ways to Promote Positive Affective Factors, available in the Instructor's area of the Online Learning Center.

Portfolio Activity 10.4 *Draw a Scientist:* Your students may have drawn their own pictures of a scientist in Chapter 1. Have your students revisit their own drawings as part of this activity. In what ways are the students' drawings similar?

Portfolio Activity 10.5 *Equitable Classroom Practices*

Classroom Organization

Portfolio Activity 10.6 *Arranging a Project-Based Science Classroom*

> Visual Resources: Table 10.3 Arranging a Classroom, available in the Instructor's area of the Online Learning Center.

Classroom Organization Diagram

Have your students diagram a classroom arrangement specific for their grade level. They can begin with the diagram in Portfolio Activity 10.6, a diagram you supply, or one based on a classroom they have observed or where they are currently teaching. You could start your students with two different diagrams, one with more and one with fewer fixed features such as windows or sinks. They should refer to Table 10.3, Arranging a Classroom, and the directions in Activity 10.6. Your students also can add or remove items from the movable features list based on their own or the observed classroom. They should make sure everything in their diagram is labeled. Then have them write a justification statement describing their reasoning behind each feature of their classroom arrangement. Have several students share their diagrams and explanations with the class.

Portfolio Activities 10.7 and 10.8 together will help your student begin planning their calendars for their project planning in the next chapter.

Portfolio Activity 10.7 *Preplanning the Number of Minutes Allocated to Subjects*

Portfolio Activity 10.8 *Scheduling*

> Visual Resources: Table 10.9 Planning Safe Lessons, available in the Instructor's area of the Online Learning Center.

Portfolio Activity 10.9 *Conducting a Safety Audit*

Management Strategies

Each of the following portfolio activities explores a specific management strategy. Your students can use these activities as components of their management plan.

Portfolio Activity 10.10 *Establishing Ground Rules*

> Visual Resources: Figure 10.2 Behavior Tree Model, available in the Instructor's area of the Online Learning Center.

Portfolio Activity 10.11 *Making a Contract*

> Visual Resources: Figure 10.4 Fish-bone Model, available in the Instructor's area of the Online Learning Center.

Portfolio Activity 10.12 *Anticipating Problems*

> Visual Resources: Table 10.12 How Did I Do?, available in the Instructor's area of the Online Learning Center.

> Visual Resources: Table 10.13 How Did Our Team Do?, available in the Instructor's area of the Online Learning Center.

Management Plan

Have your students develop a classroom management plan for a project-based classroom targeting a specific grade level. They should include specific points to address each of the three key components of the basic management of a project-based science classroom: classroom climate, organization, and management strategies. You also can ask them to address considerations before, during, and after instruction. Encourage them to use ideas and documents developed during the portfolio activities and the tables in this chapter. Have your students share their ideas with one or two other students in small groups. Then each group can share with the whole class specific features they found interesting and what they learned about management plans during their small-group discussion. Finally, your students should write a rationale statement justifying the key points in their management plans.

Tip: Novice teachers are very concerned about classroom management. Creating a management plan will reassure and prepare them for the classroom.

Portfolio Activity 10.13 *Rethinking Your Views about Managing a Project-Based Science Class:* Have your students revisit their initial ideas about classroom management. Have any ideas changed? If so, how are they different? Are any ideas still the same? How will the students' ideas impact what they will do in the classroom?

Discussion Questions

Think back to a favorite classroom from your elementary school experiences. What kinds of things did your teacher do to promote this environment? Can you remember what kinds of things the students did in this classroom? Can you relate the strategies used by the teacher in this classroom to the strategies discussed in this chapter?

Discuss how it is possible to give students "real choices," and yet maintain a classroom that is orderly and safe. What does it mean to give students real choices? How can a teacher give students real choices and still manage the classroom environment?

Some elementary school teachers feel uncomfortable about not having in-depth understandings of all science content they are expected to teach. Discuss how a teacher can promote a positive attitude toward science when he or she is apprehensive about not knowing all the answers.

Discuss how popular toys in our culture may influence girls' and boys' beliefs about their role in society. Discuss how television and other forms of media may promote stereotypes about careers for women and careers for men.

Describe the basic classroom norms you would set up in your classroom in the beginning of school. Justify how these norms can contribute to establishing a project-based environment.

How would you manage different groups of students working on different investigations in your classroom? What kinds of strategies would you use to ensure that all groups worked productively and received support from you when needed? How would you determine the progress each group made each day? How would you ensure that all members of the group contributed to the group work?

Assessment Ideas

Portfolio Assessment

The activities in this chapter are all valuable components of a management plan that your student should keep in their professional teaching portfolios to use in the future. Although your students should do each activity, you can choose one or two to evaluate from each of the three key components of classroom management: classroom climate, organization, and management strategies. Activities 10.1, *Managing a Science Classroom*, 10.3, *Promoting Positive Affective Factors*, 10.6, *Arranging a Project-Based Science Classroom*, 10.9, *Conducting a Safety Audit*, and 10.12, *Anticipating Problems*, are particularly useful to help you understand your students' ideas about managing a project-based science classroom.

Classroom Organization Diagram

Have your students diagram their ideal classroom arrangement. They should make sure they label their diagrams. Then have them write a justification statement describing the reasoning behind each feature of their classroom arrangement. They should be able to apply ideas discussed in class to create a safe, inquiry-oriented environment appropriate for their grade level.

Management Plan

Have your students develop a classroom management plan for a project-based classroom targeting a specific grade level. They should include specific points to address each of the three key components of the basic management of a project-based science classroom: classroom climate, organization, and management strategies. You also can ask them to address considerations before, during, and after instruction. Your students should write a rationale statement justifying the key points in their management plans.

Resources

Text Resources

American Association for the Advancement of Science (1990). *Science for All Americans*. New York: Oxford University Press.

American Association for the Advancement of Science (1993). *Benchmarks for Science Literacy*. New York: Oxford University Press.

National Research Council. (1996). *National Science Education Standards*. Washington, D.C.: National Academy Press.

Internet Resources

BrainPOP (http://www.brainpop.com) BrainPOP is the leading producer of animated, educational movies. The original movies explain numerous scientific concepts including the food chain. Fun, useful Web site for K-12 students because it addresses so many topics.

Carolina Biological (http://www.carolina.com): Suppliers of classroom science equipment.

ECO-USA (http://www.eco-usa.net): Web site focuses on the nation's environment. Contains information on specific environmental toxins including DDT. Also lists toxic waste sites in each state.

Flinn Scientific Company (http://www.flinnsci.com): Flinn Scientific Company page; links to school science laboratory safety.

GLIN: Great Lakes Information Network (http://www.great-lakes.net): Contains information about the Great Lakes region environment, tourism, education, and more.

National Science Teachers Association (http://www.nsta.org): NSTA Position Statement on Multicultural Science.

Tenet Web (http://www.tenet.edu/academia/multi.html): Texas Education Network, Hall of multiculturalism resource center; links to numerous multicultural resources.

U.S. Environmental Protection Agency (http://www.epa.gov): Official Web site of the EPA. Contains publications and interactive activities concerning current events, pollution, and international problems. A kids' section is also available, as are school-adaptable programs.

Chapter Overview

This chapter highlights the steps useful in the careful planning of a project-based curriculum. The important ideas and strategies developed in earlier chapters are reviewed and applied to the process of developing a project. To illustrate ideas, an example project on insects is developed throughout the chapter. First, concepts are identified and learning performances are selected. Concepts and learning performances are matched to national, state, and local standards. Concept mapping is used to organize the concepts. Second, the ways in which teachers can develop a driving question, benchmark lessons, investigations, assessments, and a calendar of activities are discussed. The process of developing a project is iterative; the steps operate in a back-and-forth process. Third, ways to locate commercial, noncommercial, household, and community resources for materials and lesson ideas are examined. Fourth, the reasons for the natural support of curriculum integration in a project-based environment are discussed. Concept mapping is again used as a planning tool for integrating the curriculum. Finally, how technology tools can help facilitate planning is discussed.

Chapter Learning Performances

- Explain the importance of factors teachers must consider when planning a project.

- Justify why concept mapping is critical to planning.

- Describe how a teacher can use a variety of resources to plan a project.

- Create a project-based unit of study.

- Compare and contrast strategies that can be used to help all students learn.

- Explain the value of integrating science across the curriculum.

Lesson Ideas

Developing a Project

This chapter is an opportunity for your students to revisit each of the aspects of project development described throughout the text and this manual. For example, in Chapter 3 students examined, critiqued, and developed driving questions. Also, your students began developing driving questions for their own projects. In this chapter, your students will revisit and revise their driving questions. Your students also have two example projects to reflect on. One is the project example *How can I predict if a boat will float?* A second example on insects is described in this chapter. In addition, this chapter includes overall considerations for projects such as planning a calendar. For some components your students may have lessons or ideas they feel are complete, while other features of their projects will still need development. Have your students use their ideas and plans from each of the preceding chapters to develop a complete project plan.

> **Tip:** Your students should work in groups of two. They can choose to develop one project between the two of them, or they can each work on their own topics

but together. This way they will be able to discuss ideas and give and receive feedback on their work.

Each of the portfolio activities here will guide your students through the process of developing their own project plans. If they did not have the opportunity to complete individual project components earlier, they can do so now. Even if your students have completed each of the activities, they should also complete the portfolio activities here. This will refresh their memories and will be a double check. In some cases additional considerations are included to help students develop a project they will be able to use in their classrooms. Your students also can use this opportunity to develop a second investigation or benchmark lesson to include in their projects. This is particularly useful for teachers who will be using their projects in the near future in their classrooms.

If your students have difficulty with any one activity such as developing driving questions or investigations, they can refer back to the appropriate chapter for more detailed descriptions, ideas for specific strategies, or techniques including tables, charts, and other resources.

Portfolio Activity 11.1 *Identifying Concepts, Specifying Learning Performances, and Matching to Curriculum Objectives:* Make sure your students have matched their concepts and learning performances to local as well as state and national objectives.

Visual Resources: Figure 11.1 Insect Concept Map, available in the Instructor's area of the Online Learning Center.

Portfolio Activity 11.2 *Turning Concepts, Learning Performances and Curriculum Objectives into Driving Questions*

One approach to Portfolio Activities 11.3, 11.4, and 11.5 is to have your students develop a benchmark lesson that explicitly supports the investigation they are developing. Likewise, the assessment can be embedded in either the benchmark or the investigation lesson. Lesson plan formats for benchmark lessons and investigations are described in the text.

Portfolio Activity 11.3 *Developing Benchmark Lessons:* Your students can develop a second benchmark lesson for their project instead of revising the lesson developed in Chapter 7 on benchmark lessons.

Portfolio Activity 11.4 *Developing an Investigation:* Your students can refine their initial investigation lessons. Alternatively, your students can develop a second investigation lesson that is more open or more structured than their first investigation lesson.

Portfolio Activity 11.5 *Developing Assessments:* Have your students develop an embedded assessment to match the learning performances in their investigation lesson. They can describe how they would assess both content and process ideas.

Developing a calendar of activities will help your students think about the sequence and flow of lessons in their projects. They can use this calendar to make sure they are addressing each of the important concepts and learning performances identified on their concept maps, that there is an appropriate number of investigations versus benchmark lessons, and that students have multiple opportunities to demonstrate their understanding.

> **Tip:** Teacher's initial calendars are typically much too short. When lesson ideas are fully developed, calendars tend to expand to about six weeks.

Portfolio Activity 11.6 *Developing a Calendar of Activities*

> Visual Resources: Table 11.1 Insect Project Calendar of Activities, available in the Instructor's area of the Online Learning Center.

Portfolio Activity 11.7 *Revisiting Your Project Design:* This step is very important and emphasizes the iterative nature of project planning.

> Visual Resources: Figure 11.2 Process of Developing a Project, available in the Instructor's area of the Online Learning Center.

Selecting and Obtaining Resources

Portfolio Activity 11.8 *Selecting Good Resources:* One way to complete this activity is to have each pair of students select a resource they think they may use and then rate this resource using Tables 11.2 and 11.3. Groups can then trade resource materials with another group. Each group then rates this second resource. Finally, each set of groups can compare and discuss their ratings for each resource.

> Visual Resources: Table 11.2 Summary of Criteria for Selecting Resources, available in the Instructor's area of the Online Learning Center.

> Visual Resources: Table 11.3 Criteria for Using Noncommercial Resources, available in the Instructor's area of the Online Learning Center.

Portfolio Activity 11.9 *Finding Resources Using the Web:* Select URLs from the list at the end of this and other chapters in this manual to include in this activity. Include sites that are matched to your students' project topics.

Portfolio Activity 11.10 *Identifying Resources in Local Stores*

> Visual Resources: Table 11.5 Resources for Materials needed in an Elementary or Middle Grades Science Classroom, available in the Instructor's area of the Online Learning Center.

Integrated Curriculum

Now that your students have a fairly well-developed project for science, this is a good time to think about how to integrate concepts from mathematics, social studies, and language arts. Have your students return to their concept maps to explore areas where embedding additional concepts makes sense. You should also bring in various professional standards documents for your students to examine. These documents include *National Science Education Standards* (NRC, 1996), *Standards for English Language Arts* (NCTE, 1996), *Curriculum Standards for Social Studies* (NCSS, 1994), and *Principles and Standards for School Mathematics* (NCTM, 2000). Each of these documents is available on-line at its respective professional organization's Web site.

> **Tip:** Some teachers will need to coordinate with other teachers at their schools in order to integrate their projects. Teachers in self-contained classrooms will be able to integrate subjects more easily.

Portfolio Activity 11.11 *Investigating Your Beliefs about Curriculum Integration*

> Visual Resources: Table 11.6 Strategies to Adapt Teaching Activities to Meet Students' Multiple Intelligences, available in the Instructor's area of the Online Learning Center.

Visual Resources: Table 11.7 Sample Multiple Intelligences Lessons on Insects, available in the Instructor's area of the Online Learning Center.

Portfolio Activity 11.12 *Developing Integrated Curriculum*

Visual Resources: Table 11.8 Rubric for Evaluating Integrated Curriculum, available in the Instructor's area of the Online Learning Center.

Visual Resources: Figure 11.4 Concept Map for Science Integration, available in the Instructor's area of the Online Learning Center.

Project Development

Have your students present their plans to the class. This is the culmination of a course-long project planning. Obviously they cannot teach or demonstrate every lesson or feature of their projects. Therefore, they will need to be creative in their presentation by using posters, multimedia documents, or other displays. You can ask them to highlight specific lessons or features that they did not complete in their initial plans. This project presentation is an opportunity for your students to illustrate their ideas for an overall plan to answer a driving question. Finally, students should write a rationale statement describing how their plan incorporates each feature of project-based science and supports students in developing understanding of important science ideas.

Discussion Questions

Discuss what is meant by an iterative process when planning a project. Choose an example of a topic area and illustrate how teachers may use the steps presented in this chapter in a different order.

Discuss how the national standards documents (*National Science Education Standards* and *Benchmarks for Scientific Literacy*) support the integration of curriculum. What are the key statements in these documents to justify teachers planning integrated curricula?

How do the terms *integrated, interdisciplinary,* and *thematic* compare? What are examples of units that illustrate these different terms? How does your understanding of these terms compare with the definitions presented in this chapter? In what ways is project-based science consistent with the definition of integrated curriculum used in this chapter?

How would you go about exploring the resources in your school community? What are the benefits of using resources in the community?

Assessment Ideas

Portfolio Assessment

You can use Activities 11.6, *Developing a Calendar of Activities*, and 11.7, *Revisiting Your Project Design*, to assess your students' understanding of a project's overall sequence and flow. Activity 11.8, *Selecting Good Resources*, is useful to see if your students can select and critique resources for their value in developing specific lessons within a project. Finally, Activity 11.12, *Developing Integrated Curriculum*, further demonstrates your students' understanding of a project's overall development and their ability to connect various concepts within a project.

Project Development

You can observe groups and individuals as they are developing an overall plan and individual components for their projects. This will give you an indication of what ideas your students find challenging. You can point them to specific resources and to appropriate descriptions in previous chapters as needed.

This is the culmination of the course-long project planning. You will have assessed individual components such as a benchmark lesson or investigation lesson earlier when these components were initially developed. Here you can evaluate just the specific components that students struggled with in their initial plans. This project plan is an opportunity for you to assess your students' abilities to develop an appropriate overall plan to answer a driving question. This plan should include some of the suggested strategies described in the text adapted for their specific lessons. In addition, students should write a rationale statement describing how their plan incorporates each feature of project-based science and supports students in developing understanding of important science ideas.

Resources

Text Resources

American Association for the Advancement of Science (1990). *Science for All Americans*. New York: Oxford University Press.

American Association for the Advancement of Science (1993). *Benchmarks for Science Literacy*. New York: Oxford University Press.

National Council for the Social Studies (1994). *Curriculum Standards for Social Studies*. Washington, D.C.: National Council for the Social Studies.

National Council of Teachers of English/International Reading Association (IRA) (1996). *Standards for English Language Arts*. Newark, DE: National Council of Teachers of English.

National Council of Teachers of Mathematics (2000). *Principles and Standards for School Mathematics*. Reston, VA: National Council of Teachers of Mathematics.

National Research Council (1996). *National Science Education Standards*. Washington, D.C.: National Academy Press.

Project WET (1995). *Project WET Curriculum and Activity Guide*. Houston, TX: The Watercourse and Council for Environmental Education.

Project Wild (1992). *Project Wild Activity Guide*. Bethesda, MD: Western Regional Environmental Education Council.

Project Wild (1992). *Aquatic Project Wild Aquatic Education Activity Guide*. Bethesda, MD: Western Regional Environmental Education Council.

Roseman, J. E., Kesidou, S., and Stern, L. (1997). *Identifying Curriculum Materials for Science Literacy: A Project 2061 Evaluation Tool*. Washington, D.C.: American Association for the Advancement of Science.

Stern, L., and Roseman, J. E. (2001). Textbook alignment. *The Science Teacher*, 68(10).

Sunburst Communications. *Voyage of the Mimi I and The Second Voyage of the Mimi.* 101 Castleton Street, P.O. Box 100, Pleasantville, NY: author.

Wiggins, G., and McTighe, J. (1998). *Understanding by Design.* Alexandria, VA: ASCD, Association for Supervision and Curriculum Development.

Internet Resources

Banana Slug String Band (http://www.bananaslugstringband.com): Information for Environmental educators, interpreters, and teachers: develop curricula and provide trainings and workshops in your schools so you can learn how to do the Water Cycle Boogie and create a rainstorm right in your classroom.

Butterfly Zone (http://www.butterflies.com): Everything about butterflies, including how to raise them in your classroom.

Carolina Biological (www.carolina.com): Suppliers of classroom science equipment.

Center for Highly Interactive Computing in Education (http://hi-ce.org): Source of project-based, technology-enhanced middle school curriculum materials.

Directory of Educational Sites (http://www.osstf.on.ca/www/links/edusort.html#Subjects-Science): Provides numerous links to multiple educational sites useful for project planning.

Eisenhower National Clearing House (http://www.enc.org): ENC identifies effective curriculum resources, creates high-quality professional development materials, and disseminates useful information and products to improve K-12 mathematics and science teaching and learning.

NASA Spacelink (http://spacelink.msfc.nasa.gov/.index.html): NASA's education division; libraries, current events, and other space-related resources.

National Academy Press (http://www.nas.edu): Includes links to entire on-line text of the *National Science Education Standards.* Browse contents and abstracts of *Proceedings of the National Academy of Sciences,* with opportunity to access thousands of scientific reports.

National Council for the Social Studies (NCSS) (http://www.ncss.org): Professional organization for teachers of social studies at all grade levels elementary to college; resource includes on-line journals—*Social Studies and the Young Learner* for elementary teachers and *Social Education* for middle grade teachers—and recommendations for teaching mathematics and position statements of NCSS.

National Council of Teachers of English (NCTE) (http://www.ncte.org): Professional organization for teachers of English studies, literacy, and language arts at all grade levels elementary to college; resource includes on-line journals—*Language Arts* for elementary and middle grade teachers—and recommendations for teaching mathematics and position statements of NCTE

National Council of Teachers of Mathematics (NCTM) (http://www.nctm.org): Professional organization for teachers of mathematics at all grade levels elementary to college; resource includes on-line journals—*Teaching Children Mathematics* for elementary teachers and *Mathematics Teaching in the Middle School* for middle grade teachers—and recommendations for teaching mathematics and position statements of NCTM.

National Science Teachers Association (NSTA) (http://www.nsta.org): Professional organization for teachers of science at all grade levels elementary to college; resource includes on-line journals—*Science and Children* for elementary science teachers and *Science Scope* for middle grade science teachers—and recommendations for teaching science and position statements of NSTA.

National Wildlife Federation (http://www.nwf.org/education/): Environmental education resources; school and community programs.

One Sky, Many Voices (www.onesky.umich.edu): Science curricula that utilize CD-ROM and the World Wide Web; program centered on environmental science themes run during a set time period to coordinate learning among participants.

Project 2061 (http://www.project2061.org/default.htm): Describes Project 2061 background and goals and the guiding document, *Science for All Americans*; links to on-line text of *Benchmarks for Science Literacy*; links to on-line text of *Blueprints*, description of Resources for Science Literacy.

Raffi Children's Singer (http://www.raffinews.com): Children's music, new and classics.

TERC (http://www.terc.edu/): Not-for-profit education research and development organization; mission is to improve mathematics, science, and technology teaching and learning; research and development of curriculum materials.

Web-Based Inquiry Science Environment (WISE) (http://wise.berkeley.edu/welcome.php): Technology-enhanced projects.

CHAPTER 12
WHAT ARE THE NEXT STEPS?

Chapter Overview

This final chapter summarizes each of the features of project-based science presented in the previous chapters. This chapter highlights the benefits and the challenges of using this teaching approach. Strategies for how teachers can overcome these challenges include using students' projects to gain more knowledge, reading and conferences, and using the World Wide Web. A number of real and perceived pressures that teachers face when using project-based science, including the tension between trying to cover a broad array of science topics and giving students time to carry out long-term investigations, are addressed.

The final sections of the chapter focus on the need for professional growth of a teacher and suggest strategies that include reflection and action research. Opportunities for professional development include memberships in professional organizations, reading publications, accessing the World Wide Web, and participating in conferences, field trips, and workshops. Finally, students are asked to reflect on their initial driving questions developed in Chapter 1 and to reexamine their portfolio assembled while using this book.

Chapter Learning Performances

- Summarize the key features of project-based science.

- Explain the important benefits of using project-based science.

- Describe how a teacher can continue his or her professional development.

- Create a professional development plan.

- Compare and contrast the challenges to implementing a project-based curriculum and specify strategies that can be used to overcome challenges.

- Critique how you have grown professionally by examining your portfolio.

Lesson Ideas

Summary of Project-Based Science

This is an excellent time to have your students create a concept map of project-based science. First, your students should revisit their concept maps of science from Chapter 1 and how students learn from Chapter 2. Have a short discussion in groups or as a whole class to revisit their original ideas. Students can identify ideas that have or have not changed and why. They will then be able to incorporate ideas from their original maps into this new map of project-based science. Although your students previously worked in groups to develop maps, here they should create individual maps to illustrate their own ideas about project-based science. Finally, they should write a reflection statement based on their maps describing how project-based science is or is not consistent with science and how students learn science.

In the next two sections your students will be discussing benefits and challenges of project-based science. You may decide to have them complete their concept maps and write reflection statements after Portfolio Activities 12.1 and 12.2. Then your students will be able to incorporate ideas from these discussions into their maps and statements about the nature of project-based science.

Benefits of Project-Based Science

Portfolio Activity 12.1 *Benefits of Project-Based Science:* Your students can include some of their ideas discussed here in their reflection statements for their project-based science concept maps.

Challenges of Project-Based Science

Portfolio Activity 12.2 *Your Challenges:* Your students can include some of their ideas discussed here in their reflection statements for their project-based science concept maps.

Continuing Your Professional Growth

Encourage your students to participate in one or more of the professional activities suggested in the text. For example, you can encourage your students to apply for student memberships in the National Science Teachers Association.

You also could have your students select and read two articles pertaining to science learners' understanding of a particular science concept or an activity designed to teach a particular science concept from any professional journal for science teachers, and write a summary of each article. The journals they might select include *Science and Children, Science Scope,* and *School Science and Mathematics.*

Another idea is to encourage your students to attend a science district, regional, or science in-service day in which they participate in work sessions or view exhibits. Ask your students to write a reflective log of their experiences. What things did they learn? Did they engage in any conversations with other teachers? Have your students share their reactions to the in-service day.

Finally, you could invite one or more teachers who use a project-based science approach in teaching elementary or middle school science to participate in a panel discussion or presentation. Ask teachers to bring examples of student products and samples of handouts.

Action Plan

Have your students develop a plan for how they will use a project-based science approach to teaching science in their classrooms. This includes a description and justification of their goals and how they plan to implement their ideas. They should consider the benefits and challenges of project-based science and their own professional growth. Reflection on their own teaching should be highlighted in their plans. Your students should focus on their first year of teaching, but also include some long-range plans.

Inquiry into Your Teaching

A good way to conclude your course is to have students revisit and reflect on ideas throughout their portfolios. Give your students time to go through their portfolios with a partner or in small groups of three or four. One idea to guide their conversation is to have students use this time to select the components that best illustrate their developing understanding. This would include pieces that show initial ideas and how those ideas changed, as well as descriptions of what supported their learning. Once these components are selected, your students can arrange them together with a description of the learning they illustrate. Other components can be included in the back or an appendix. You also can use Portfolio Activities 12.3 and 12.4 to guide small-group discussions.

Portfolio Activity 12.3 *Revisiting Initial Ideas in Your Portfolio:* The questions in this activity can be completed individually or can be used for small-group or whole-class discussion. Students should reflect on their portfolios individually before participating in a small-group or whole-class discussion.

Portfolio Activity 12.4 *Reexamining Your Portfolio:* The questions in this activity can be completed individually and then shared in small-group or whole-class discussion.

Discussion Questions

What are the main features of a project-based approach to teaching science? Which of these factors did you find different from your perspective on teaching elementary science at the beginning of this course? In what ways have your ideas changed about teaching science in elementary and middle school?

Which of the challenges in developing a project-based science classroom do you anticipate to be the most difficult to overcome? What kinds of steps can you take to address these challenges?

What are some useful World Wide Web sites you found related to creating a project-based classroom? How could you continue to use the Web in your planning and instruction?

With all the demands of day-to-day teaching, how is it possible to keep up with all the new science discoveries? What are some sources of information about scientific discoveries that may be understandable and useful to an elementary or middle school science teacher?

How can you deal with the dilemma of lack of time in planning a project-based science curriculum? What are some strategies to use in developing a curriculum that promotes meaningful, in-depth learning, but not at the expense of learning key science concepts?

Assessment ideas

Any one of the assessment ideas describe below can be used in place of a final exam. You can use the final exam time for presentations or as additional time for final discussions and questions.

Portfolio Assessment

All of the activities in this chapter are useful in assessing your students' overall understanding of project-based science and how this approach supports student learning. In addition, Activities 12.3, *Revisiting Initial Ideas in Your Portfolio*, and 12.4, *Reexamining Your Portfolio*, support your assessment of students' portfolios. In both of these activities students revisit their entries and reflect on their learning. You can ask students to select and include only those entries that best illustrate their learning over the course of the semester. Another idea is to set up appointment times for your students to present their portfolios to you individually or in pairs. You could ask them to defend their reasons for including particular pieces of work in their portfolios.

Project-Based Science Concept Map

Your students' concept maps can be evaluated for their understanding of project-based science. You can evaluate maps for completeness and complexity. Are there aspects of project-based science obviously missing from the map? Is the map linear, or is it weblike, showing an integrated understanding? Are the links appropriate? Is there an appropriate hierarchy? Also, read their reflection statements describing how project-based science is or is not consistent with science and how students learn science.

Action Plan

Have your students develop a plan for how they will use a project-based science approach to teaching science in their classrooms. They should describe and justify their goals and how they plan to implement their ideas. They should consider the benefits and challenges of project-based science and their own professional growth. Your students should focus on their first year of teaching, but also include some long-range plans. You can assess their plans for appropriate goals, specific steps they could take, and how they could evaluate their own progress addressing their goals.

Resources

Text Resources

American Association for the Advancement of Science. (1990). *Science for All Americans*. New York: Oxford University Press.

American Association for the Advancement of Science. (1993). *Benchmarks for Science Literacy*. New York: Oxford University Press.

National Research Council. (1996). *National Science Education Standards*. Washington, D.C.: National Academy Press.

Internet Sites

Eisenhower National Clearinghouse (http://www.enc.org): Teachers can sign up for Digital Dozen and daily education headlines email updates.

Every Child a Scientist (http://www.nap.edu/catalog/6005.html): On-line text of *Every Child a Scientist: Achieving Scientific Literacy for All*.

Lab-Net (http://www.netlab.org): A community of peers, scientists, and explorers striving to provide students, teachers, and professionals in the realm of science with the opportunity to experience such things as virtual projects, intellectual discussions, and much more.

National Board for Professional Teaching Standards (http://www.nbpts.org): National board certification; set standards for teachers, strengthened their educational preparation through the standards, and created performance-based assessments that demonstrate accomplished application of the standards.

National Science Education Standards (http://www.nap.edu): On-line text of the national standards; includes professional development standards.

National Science Foundation (http://www.nsf.gov): Reports from funded research in science, mathematics, engineering, and education.